AIP Manual

The Autoimmune Protocol Plan With 89 Delicious Paleo Recipes to Treat Inflammation

Written by Dr. Marcus T. Fraser
V1.

Disclaimer

The recipes provided in this report are for informational purposes only and are not intended to provide dietary advice. A medical practitioner should be consulted before making any changes in your diet. Additionally, recipe cooking times may require adjustment depending on age and quality of appliances.

Readers are strongly urged to take all precautions to ensure ingredients are fully cooked in order to avoid the dangers of foodborne viruses. The recipes and suggestions provided in this book are solely the opinion of the author.

The author and publisher do not take any responsibility for any consequences that may result due to following the instructions provided in this book.

Table of Contents

An AIP-Proof Diet and its Benefits

Every day, dozens of people get diagnosed with one or more autoimmune conditions: systemic lupus erythematosus, celiac disease, Graves' disease, rheumatoid arthritis, or type 1 diabetes. All of these conditions and many more are caused by a dysfunction of the immune system. Normally, the immune system is responsible for fighting off microorganisms such as viruses, bacteria, and fungi that would otherwise invade the human body. However, some people's immune systems have difficulty differentiating between self and non-self. Essentially, their immune systems attack their own body tissues, mistaking them as foreign material. Some auto-immune diseases destroy the intestines, while others destroy joints, organs, skin, or glands.

Scientists don't know the exact reasons for these attacks healthy body tissues. What is known is that many autoimmune reactions are in fact a response to a trigger: drugs, viruses, bacteria, irritants, food, etc. For example, someone with celiac disease will suffer intestinal damage after eating food that contains gluten (a protein element present in barley, wheat, and rye). Other people are sensitive to specific vegetables, chemicals, or environmental triggers that cause heavy inflammation in their joints. In other words, autoimmune conditions seem to be similar to allergies in cause, but they have chronic consequences, whereas allergies result in immediate, passing reactions after contact with allergens.

This leads the scientific community to further try to understand the role of inflammation in autoimmunity. Research suggests that there are certain foods that trigger some of these autoimmune reactions. Such foods have toxins or proteins believed to cause inflammation and prompt the autoimmune reactions. The inflammation and autoimmune reactions have led nutritionists to design a restrictive diet eliminating foods that can cause inflammation. The foods are later reintroduced one at a time to identify the exact foods that cause the inflammation. This strategic diet is commonly referred to as the autoimmune protocol (AIP).

Autoimmune diet protocol (AIP) falls under the broad dieting umbrella of the Paleo diet. It is a stricter version of the Paleo diet that involves beginning with the basic Paleo diet and eliminating a few other foods in addition to the Paleo restrictions. Foods avoided on the autoimmune protocol are those that have been shown to aggravate leaky gut, Scleroderma, and celiac disease, among others. A break from these foods gives the stomach lining a chance to heal if it has incurred damage as a result of sensitivity to these foods. After spending 30-60 days on AIP, you can begin the process of systematic re-introduction of eliminated foods. Reintroduction depends on the improvement of an individual's symptoms. If after 30-60 days there are no improvements, keep going. The goal is to identify which foods have a negative effect on the body, so total recovery is necessary before testing the different foods. Via re-introduction you'll gradually return to a Paleo diet. Later, remove any re-introduced foods that caused problems.

The autoimmune protocol is aimed at ensuring a person's immune system gets enough rest, lowering the levels of inflammation and allowing for the recovery process. When the levels of inflammation are reduced and the healing of the gut happens, you can reintroduce foods gradually, monitoring any autoimmune outbursts that may happen. Since the AIP is fairly limited, most people are happy to be able to reintroduce foods.

The autoimmune diet is meant to tackle four different issues within the body:

- *Regulating the immune system:* reintroduce necessary microorganisms to the gut, repair the barrier that serves as the gut lining, and provide the micronutrients that the immune system needs to function properly.

- *Regulating hormones:* to regulate the immune system and, in the long term, to allow the hormones to self-regulate.

- *Improving gut health:* repair the lining of the gastrointestinal tract to stop leaky gut syndrome and therefore the inflammation caused by the food particles entering the bloodstream.

- *Providing a wealth of nutrients:* consume more nutrient-dense foods to fuel the body and the immune system and correct any imbalances or deficiencies that inhibit the immune system.

Food as Medicine

The discordance between the ancient human genome and today's contemporary diets and lifestyles is the underlying cause behind all autoimmune disorders afflicting humans today. This hypothesis is bolstered by the fact that these diseases did not exist before agriculture changed the diet and lifestyle of primitive man. Additionally, these diseases are also virtually absent or extremely rare among hunter-gatherer societies and non-westernized populations today. Certain foods contribute to severe patho-physiological consequences. What happens in the digestive system when these foods are ingested? Which foods are high-risk for autoimmune reactions? The best foods provide nutrients that the body needs. Apart from the nutritional value, foods can be evaluated based on whether they contain any foreign substances that alter the functioning of the gut, or antigens that trick the immune system into releasing antibodies to react against the body itself, causing inflammation.

There is a lot of truth to the old saying, "you are what you eat." What is ingested to the body plays a huge part in how the body functions. A diet high in fat and sodium may result retaining too much fat and sodium in the body, leading to obesity and high blood pressure. On the other hand, foods that are high in protein, fiber, and healthy nutrients are essential for the body to be strong and well-regulated. This wisdom also applies to autoimmune diseases; there are certain foods that are good at fighting autoimmune diseases while others can stimulate the infections.

Food is an important source of calories, or energy, as well as important phytonutrients, fatty acids, antioxidants, minerals, and vitamins. Food also plays a big role in other functions like regulating blood sugar levels, improving the cardiovascular health, regulating inflammation, aiding the digestive organs, and much more.

Diet can cause illnesses or maintain health until old age. Diets influence such diseases as cancer, heart disease, diabetes, allergies, and autoimmune ailments like arthritis.

Food can act as medicinal protectors against a number of ailments:

Controlling and Decreasing the Effects of Inflammation. Inflammation is the major cause of a number of diseases and makes people age faster. Inflammation affects all parts of the body including cells, tissues, and hormones. With the right foods, inflammation can be managed easily.

Hormonal Balancing. Hormones play a major part in normal functioning of the body. Hormones affect energy production, brain function, weight management, and even sex drive. Hormone imbalance can trigger certain processes that aggravate the body and result in obesity, low mental capabilities, diabetes, autoimmune diseases, premature aging, depression, reproduction issues, and fatigue.

Alkalizing the Body. For normal and optimal functioning of the body, the pH has to be maintained at around 7.36. Ingesting too many processed foods raises your acid level, making it easier for infections to thrive. Foods with alkaline properties act as detoxifiers to renew the worn-out cells and promote longevity.

Balancing Blood Glucose (Sugar). Poor response to insulin and other related hormones may result in weight gain and diabetes. Processed carbs and sugar ingested in high amounts may result into mood disorders, fatigue, hormonal imbalances, damage to neurons, and even cravings. To maintain normal blood sugar levels, seek out non-processed carbs and foods that have a low glycemic index.

Removing Toxins. When there are issues in the digestive system, toxicity may occur. Other causes can include liver failure and hormone imbalance. Certain foods let the body detoxify and thus avoid the problems that toxins can cause, such as fibromyalgia, infertility, autoimmune ailments, and inflammation.

Improved Nutrient Absorption. Poor foods lead to nutrient-deficiency and free radical damage, both of which cause various other ailments. Processed foods are usually low in nutrients. Most unprocessed foods are rich in nutrients like antioxidants, vitamins, enzymes, minerals, and fiber.

Autoimmune Diseases & Inflammation

An autoimmune disease can be defined as a condition in which the body's normal immune processes, which combat the onslaught of invading antigens—viruses, bacteria, or parasites—rejects specific parts of the body itself, as if acting on a foreign invader. An autoimmune reaction can target any organ in the body if the antibodies released by the immune system can't differentiate between healthy body tissues and invading antigens. These diseases are characterized by inflammation and destruction of body tissues by one's own immune system.

An autoimmune disease is usually triggered by the immune system failing to distinguish between proteins that belong to the human body and those that belong to an unfamiliar invader, such as a virus, bacteria, or parasite. The body struggles to protect itself against a threat like an infection, toxin, allergen, or even certain foods, and it doesn't discern the enemy from other parts of the body. Since the immune system is now stressed, it triggers antibodies to mistakenly attack the body tissues instead of the invaders. A variety of symptoms can result, but particularly an increased number of damaged tissues and cells. The specific cells or proteins that are targeted defines each disease. For example, when tissues in the joints are attacked, it will result in rheumatoid arthritis; when the thyroid is attacked, it causes hypo- or hyper-thyroiditis. However, the root cause is always the same.

Some of the autoimmune diseases include:

- **Psoriasis**: affects the skin, causing an overproduction of skin cells that creates red, itchy, painful patches over the entire body. Can also cause arthritis.

- **Rheumatoid arthritis**: a disease of the immune system that attacks the joints. Can also attack the lungs, kidneys, and blood vessels.

- **Scleroderma**: causes the blood vessels and connective tissue to grow abnormally, causing trouble swallowing, shortness of breath, skin abnormalities, etc.

- **Inflammatory Bowel Disease (IBD)**: chronic inflammation in part or all of the digestive tract. Includes Crohn's disease and ulcerative colitis. Can cause abdominal pain, vomiting, bloating, diarrhea, rectal bleeding, etc.

- **Sjogren's Syndrome**: attacks moisture-producing glands and is identified by two of its most common symptoms, dry mouth and dry eyes. Can also attack other areas such as the lungs, kidneys, and neurological system.

- **Multiple Sclerosis**: develops when the protective coating or sheath around the nerves along the spinal cord are damaged by the immune system.

- **Lupus**: can attack many parts to the body, including skin, joints, blood vessels and kidneys.

- **Hashimoto's Disease**: causes the thyroid gland to under produce thyroid hormones.

- **Transplant Rejection:** in a transplant operation, if the organ recipient's immune system rejects the donated organ, inflammation occurs in the transplanted organ and in the surrounding tissues.

- **Various Allergic Reactions:** All allergic reactions cause inflammation. Asthma causes inflammation of the airways, hay fever causes inflammation in nose, ear, throat, and mucous membranes.

- **Type 1 Diabetes:** results from little or no insulin production in the pancreas. If diabetes is left unchecked and not managed appropriately, inflammation in various parts of the body can develop quickly.

- **Celiac Disease**: involves destruction of the celia and inflammation in the inner lining of the small intestine.

Many autoimmune diseases have no cure and very few treatment options, as they are not well understood. Medical research has made great progress in recent years, but many doctors are beginning to encourage those who suffer from autoimmune diseases to make simple lifestyle changes to help boost their body's immune system. Hopefully, this will improve the body's response when the autoimmune disease goes on the attack.

So, if a diet that was designed to assist the body's immune system could decrease the symptoms or effects of an autoimmune disease, why wait until one is officially diagnosed with an autoimmune disease? Why not adopt this diet and lifestyle today?

This diet is about leading a healthy life and giving the body the tools it needs to reduce inflammation, fight disease, and create the strongest immune system possible.

What Causes Autoimmune Diseases?

About a third of one's predisposition to autoimmune diseases comes from genetic factors, while the other two thirds come from factors such as lifestyle, hormones, diet, weight, and consistent exposure to toxins and chemicals, among others. While there is no way to control genetic predisposition, everyone has total control over the desired lifestyle and diet affecting weight, hormones, and even the exposure to toxins and chemicals. How is this possible?

The truth is, all individuals can benefit from a healthy diet that allows the body to heal itself and boosts the immune system. Good news is also that the immune system can be stopped from attacking the body and create a conducive environment suitable to healing. Remember, this book is not a substitute for medical advice. Consult a professional or doctor before using the suggested remedies in the book.

Risk Factors and Contributing Factors

Autoimmune diseases can affect anyone, but certain people are at more at risk than others. Factors such as gender, race, genetics, environment, and age are considered vital in developing autoimmune diseases.

Genetic Factors

Genetic predisposition is a major factor that can put one at risk of developing an autoimmune disease. About one third of patients suffering from an autoimmune disorder has at least one relative who suffers from the same affliction.

Some of these disorders run in families with higher prevalence, like in the case of multiple sclerosis, diabetes, and lupus. Moreover, different types of autoimmune disorders can also affect the members of a single family. Certain genes are thought to be the culprit for getting the disorder, but a combination of genes can trigger it the start of symptoms.

Currently, there are at least 68 different genetic risk factors that have been proven in scientific studies, however the problem lies in the unpredictability of the gene expression. The existint studies have only proved that there is an increased risk of developing an autoimmune disorder. It does not have to be the same disorder that was exhibited by the family member who passed on the gene.

Environmental Factors

One may not have control over the genetic predisposition, but the environmental factors that expose one to the risk of developing an autoimmune disease can be controlled. A healthy diet and avoidence of risk factors can decrease one's chance of developing symptoms.

Environmental factors have a proven role in the development of autoimmune diseases. The exact triggers and how their interactions with genetic factors cause disorders are not yet known. Many of the environmental risk factors that have been located are infections agents, stress, hormones, and drug use. For instance, exposure to certain medications like hydrolyzine and procainamide, or to metals like silver, gold, or mercury can increase the risk of disease. Likewise, too much sun exposure, solvents, bacterial and viral infections are linked to autoimmune problems.

Infectious Agents

Studies have been conducted on various animal models that have provided some of the best evidence of infectious agents triggering autoimmune disease. During these studies, researchers theorized that the immune response was triggered by antigens of microorganisms that resemble self-antigens, a theory currently referred to as "molecular mimicry."

A second theory is that autoimmunity is induced by a mechanism, known as the "bystander effect." This is where the invading microorganism directly contributes to the (active) infection.

The typical diseases that are associated with infection as the main impetus are:

- Multiple sclerosis
- Type 1 diabetes
- Rheumatoid arthritis
- Systemic lupus
- Fibromyalgia
- Myasthenia gravis
- Guillain-Barre syndrome

The microorganisms that are typically to blame for the activation of these diseases are viral. The viruses include:

- Epstein-Barr
- Hepatitis C
- Parvo Virus
- Cytmealovirus

Stress

In several human and animal studies, stress was also proven to be a trigger for autoimmune diseases. Stress can cause the immune system to react in a lot of different ways, including causing alterations in the way that the immune system moderates itself. As a result, scientists and researchers have deducted that stress may be an active factor in the development of abnormal immune responses. There are certain autoimmune diseases that are more likely to be triggered by stress, such as systemic lupus, rheumatoid arthritis, and fibromyalgia. The scientific studies lacked the power to determine how much stress can actually affect the predominance of autoimmune diseases.

Reproductive Hormones

Reproductive hormones and the metabolites and receptors that are involved in their regulation and lifespan may cause an immunoregulation response. They also play roles in the maturation of lymphocytes and the activation and synthesis of antibodies and cytokines.

The reason scientists and researchers feel that sex hormones are a factor in autoimmunity dysregulation are that individuals with autoimmune diseases have some form of hormone deficit. Also, in women, most flares occur around the time of menstruation or during pregnancy. However, more extensive research is necessary to determine how much of a role reproductive hormones play in the manifestation of an autoimmune disease, or the advancement of the disease itself.

Gender

Women are more commonly affected by autoimmune diseases, especially during childbearing age. It is still not clear why women are more prone to acquire the disorders but there were speculations pointing to women's more developed immune system. Such enhancement makes them more vulnerable to these disorders, as well as hormonal changes.

Previous Infection

Inconclusive research suggests that people who have already experienced viral and bacterial infections are more susceptible to autoimmune disorders

Cigarette Smoking

Studies have shown that those who smoke, or are exposed to cigarette smoke, are at greater risk of developing an autoimmune disease. The most common autoimmune diseases that are triggered by smoking or second-hand smoke are rheumatic diseases, systemic lupus, and thyroiditis. Toxins present in the cigarette smoke are known to trigger an autoimmune response in many people.

Salt

A study from New England shows that a high-salt diet can increase a person's risk of developing autoimmune diseases such as multiple sclerosis. The scientists found out that when an enzyme was exposed to salt, the regular immune cells developed into pathogenic cells. These pathogens eject inflammatory proteins that have been linked to autoimmune diseases.

On average, Americans consume 50% more salt than the recommended amount, per government and nutritionists' guidelines. But despite the good arguments being presented for lowering salt intake, its connection to autoimmune diseases prevention still needs more research.

Future Research

Other risk factors are still in the early stages of research, including exposure to crystalline silica, solvents, and UV radiation. There have also been recent research studies on the timing of exposure (fetal perinatal, prepuberty, puberty, adulthood, etc.) and how that affects symptoms. Unfortunately these studies did not yield a great deal of information.

Currently, scientist and researchers are starting to understand how autoimmunity plays a vital role in having other chronic disease such as cardiovascular disease. The National Institute of Health has founded the Autoimmunity Centers of Excellence to foster research in various areas such as vulgaris, multiple sclerosis, lupus, rheumatoid arthritis, and scleroderma. The goal is to promote collaborative research across medical specialties and scientific disciplines to found efficient treatments and effective approaches.

How does Autoimmune Protocol Work?

Paleolithic diet is sometimes known as Stone Age diet, or the hunter-gather diet. The diet largely consists of foods assumed to have been consumed by human beings before the introduction of agriculture. It is believed that Paleolithic period began approximately 2.6 million years ago when humans started using stone tools. The emergence of agriculture marked the end of that period. The main components of the Paleo diet include wild animals and uncultivated plants. A good example of this diet are foods like vegetables, fish, fruits, eggs, roots, meat, and nuts. The diet does not include dairy products, grains, refined sugar, salt, legumes, and processed oils. Current studies of Paleolithic diet show that this diet prevents obesity and metabolic syndrome. (https://www.ncbi.nlm.nih.gov/pmc/articles/PMC458 8744). One of the essential ingredients commonly missing in this diet is calcium.

By eliminating processed foods, which are the major source of sodium in most western diets, you can minimize consumption of sodium. Most Paleo eaters manage a low-sodium diet without realizing it. This plan also provides a high amount of potassium. The combination of low sodium and high potassium is a recipe for a good vascular health, reducing the chance of high blood pressure.

The Paleolithic diet also improves glucose tolerance. Research conducted showed that Paleolithic diet results in a slimmer waist circumference and better glycemic control compared to other popular diets, such as Mediterranean diet. It has also been found that contemporary Paleo diets slow or prevent atherosclerosis.

This field of atherosclerosis is not yet fully understood because of its complex interaction with different environmental and genetic factors. However, most doctors recommend that their patients observe the Paleo diet to prevent this disease or better control it. A modern-day Paleo diet elevates LDL and reduces triglycerides in the blood. The net consequence is that this blood profile lessens the risk for the heart and atherosclerosis.

Clinical trials have shown that Paleo diet is an optimum diet that can easily lower the risk of blood pressure and cardiovascular disease, help with weight loss, reduce acne and markers of inflammation, and promote optimum health and athletic performance. Scientists have carried out several studies on this diet that show it improves glycemic control and other cardiovascular risk factors better than a diabetes diet in a cohort of patients with type 2diabetes.

The Paleo diet is geared toward healing the intestinal mucosa as well as supporting low inflammation in the body, which can temper the fires of an autoimmune flare up. Autoimmune disease can truly affect every part of the body if proper care and diet is not taken seriously. Paleo diet helps the body's immune response to defend the body against foreign invaders, infection, or injury. It also helps in the management of autoimmune diseases as it reduces pain, slows progression of the disease, as well as boosts the immune system.

Most of the foods in a Paleo diet contain fiber, making digestion easier and faster for the stomach and improving the metabolism. This diet contains a full balanced diet, improving general. Someone using this diet is unlikely to experience any kind of malnutrition. The rate of nutrient intake from the intestine to the bloodstream is also increased.

Summarized

The Autoimmune Protocol works trying to address four major areas considered to be the key causes of the chronic and other related autoimmune diseases. The AIP diet targets:

1. **Nutrient density.** For proper and normal functioning, every part of the human body needs to get adequate supply of antioxidants, minerals, amino acids, vitamins and essential fatty acids. Such are the building blocks of the body parts. Autoimmune diseases may occur as a result of deficiencies and imbalances in micronutrients. Whenever people ingest foods that are dense in nutrients, there is adequate supply of the micronutrients that ensures the imbalances and deficiencies are taken care of, thereby regulating such body systems like hormonal, detoxification and immunity and the production of neurotransmitters.

2. **Gut health.** Major contributors to autoimmune ailments include leaky gut and gut dysbiosis. The AIP approved foods are supposed to ensure there is healthy growth and support healthy gut microorganisms. Such foods are aimed at restoring the proper functioning of the gut and promote quick healing.

3. **Hormone regulation.** The production and existence of hormones in the human immunity system are determined by the foods ingested, feeding times and the amount of food taken. Dietary factors like too much sugars impairs the hormones thus making the immune system to weaken. AIP foods aim at regulating or promoting hormone production to stabilize the immune system.

4. **Immune system regulation.** From the above discussions, AIP foods are essential are provision of important nutrients, promoting healthy growth of gut microorganisms, enhancing normal functioning of the gut, and the regulation of hormones. Such measures in turn ensure that the immune system is regulated.

Who Stands to Benefit from an AIP Diet?

People with autoimmune diseases
It has been observed that the autoimmune protocol is effective against IBDs like ulcerative colitis and Crohn's disease. This is after a 2017 survey in which the AIP was administered to 15 patients who had suffered for 19 years. The results showed the patients returned to normal status.

Individuals with high sensitivities to foods

It is hard to track the food one eats in a day or week. Odd symptoms may be experienced and associated with diet, like grogginess, stuffy nose, itchiness, and rashes. Following the AIP diet is the way to go, eliminating the foods that can cause health issues and embracing the non-reactive foods. Once symptoms fade away after several weeks of adhering to the protocol, the phase of reintroducing foods starts. If the symptoms return, then they are matched with the particular reintroduced food.

Effects of Following the Protocol

The AIP diet is considered a healing diet with the aim of restoring integrity of the gut and ensure inflammation is reduced. AIP diet reduces symptoms of autoimmune diseases and improves an individual's health.

The AIP diet influences the beneficial bacteria located in the gut that impact symptom severity when an autoimmune disease is present.

With the AIP diet, it will be easier to determine which kind of food triggers symptoms in the body.

The body benefits from the nutritious foods ingested since the diet has a focus on anti-inflammatory foods that are unprocessed and rich in nutrients.

The diet reduces the risk of acquiring cardiovascular diseases, as the foods included in this diet are low in fat and cholesterol.

The autoimmune Paleo diet also helps improve blood sugar and proper functioning of the pancreas, thus helping patients who are suffering from or at risk for developing type 1 diabetes.

The low-calorie foods in this diet can also help you maintain a healthy weight.

This diet can help improve the conditions of people suffering from sclerosis, ulcerative colitis, lupus, celiac disease, and Crohn's disease.

The autoimmune Paleo diet is an effective diet regimen for people who are suffering from autoimmune diseases. It is also significant to consider that the AIP diet is not all about counting calories or carbs. Instead, it focuses on eating the right types of food that will help improve general well-being as well as longevity.

AIP Principles/Guidelines

- Eat a daily minimum of 25g of fiber.

How does a fiber-rich diet help with inflammation? It nourishes the body with the naturally occurring anti-inflammatory phytonutrients that are found in veggies, fruits, and other natural and whole foods. Foods such as okra, whole grains, eggplant, bananas, onions, dark leafy greens, and blueberries have a high fiber content.

- Eat a daily minimum of 9 servings of fruits and veggies.

One serving is a cup of raw leafy veggies or half cup of fruit or cooked veggies. You can add an extra anti-inflammatory punch by adding natural herbs and spices, such as ginger or turmeric, to the veggies for extra antioxidative power.

- Eat at least 4 servings of crucifers and alliums weekly.

Alliums include leeks, scallions, garlic, and onions; and crucifers include broccoli, brussels sprouts, cauliflower, cabbage, and mustard greens.
Alliums and crucifers have very powerful antioxidant qualities that play a major role in lowering the risk of cancer and other chronic illnesses.

- No more than ten percent of daily calories should come from saturated fat.

Limiting the intake of saturated fats naturally reduces the risk of heart disease by lowering levels of bad cholesterol. Additionally, one should limit intake of red meat to three small servings every week. It's recommended to marinate with natural herbs and spices and unsweetened, tart, fruit juices. This helps to reduce the number of toxic compounds that are formed during the cooking process.
Eat wild, fresh fish at least 3 times a week.
Variety is the spice of life so, when choosing fish, include a combination of cold-water, fatty fish such as mackerel, anchovies, salmon, sardines, and trout; and low-fat fish such as flounder and sole. Wild-caught fish is a rich source of clean protein and fats.

- Omega-3 fats rule!

Scientists have demonstrated that omega-3 fats significantly reduce inflammation and lower the risk of chronic illnesses like cancer, arthritis, and heart disease, which are mainly caused by inflammation.

Aim to include foods that are rich in omega-3 fats in the diet. Good sources of omega-3 fats include: flax meal, soy, oysters, salmon, herring, sardines, trout, and anchovies.

- Choose fats wisely.

Fat is indispensable to proper body function but choose fats that are going to provide actual benefits and not burden the body with disease. Canola oil and olive oil (extra virgin) are the best oils for fighting inflammation. Also use high oleic, cold-pressed safflower or sunflower oils and avocado oil.

- Eat small, healthy, regular meals – ideally 5-6 per day.

Start with a healthy, high-fiber breakfast to jump-start the day and keep the stomach full until about 10:00 or 11:00am, when you should have a mid-morning snack of fruit or coconut yogurt.
Lunch with a healthy salad or other light and healthy meal. At about 3:00 or 4:00pm, have a mid-afternoon snack of a handful of berries or fruit.
Have supper at around 7:00 or 8:00pm and optionally a late-night snack of berries.
Eating small, regular meals allows one to keep hunger at bay. This way you'll avoid the temptation to consume unhealthy foods when ravenously hungry. Eating frequent, healthy meals keeps one full for longer and on a healthy path.

- Ditch all processed foods, including refined sugars.

Processed foods include grains that have been stripped of bran and other nutrients to make them more digestible. Unfortunately, a lot of nutrients are lost in the process and artificial ingredients are added to improve taste.
Any type of food that contains a lot of sodium or high fructose corn syrup should be avoided at all costs as they contribute to inflammation.

Stay away from all artificial sweeteners and refined sugars. The last thing you want is insulin resistance, which leads to high blood pressure or type 2 diabetes, among other chronic illnesses.

- Ditch all trans fats.

The only way to do this is by learning to read food labels. Stay away from any food with labels like "vegetable shortening," "partially hydrogenated," or "hydrogenated," and most margarines. Be wary of ingredients you can't identify or pronounce. Cookies, crackers, and chips are great examples of foods that are usually doused in trans fats.

- Flavor food using natural herbs and spices. Sweeten meals with nutrient-rich fruits.

Fruits and veggies are very well endowed with phytonutrients and are anti-inflammatory. If you have a sweet tooth, use berries, apricots, apples, and carrots to naturally sweeten the food and add a healthy punch.

Cinnamon, cloves, sage, turmeric, ginger, thyme, and rosemary are some of the herbs and spices that are well-known for their anti-inflammatory properties and that will also transform the meal to pro-chef status.

A healthy body all starts with food. Make healthy food choices, drink lots of water, and lead the healthiest and most vibrant life, free of inflammation.

The Paleo Approach

From the earlier section:
Autoimmune diet protocol (AIP) aims to heal and strengthen the digestive tract lining and immune system. The major focus is on body-nourishing foods and reducing the symptoms of autoimmune diseases. Being a variation of Paleo, AIP adheres to the Paleo principles and goes ahead for a 30-day temporary elimination phase. Apart from avoiding the non-Paleo foods, others like sugars, refined oils, processed foods, legumes, pseudo-grains, eggs, alcohol and gluten are eliminated for the 30-day period. The temporary elimination is to identify the elements that bring about food intolerances.

Adhering to the Paleo Approach diet calls for an increased ingesting of foods that are rich in nutrients and promote the health. At the same time, foods that are known to trigger any related diseases are to be avoided at all costs. The rules included in the approach include:

- Eating meat, fish, seafood and poultry
- Embrace the intake of vegetables and fruits
- Make use of quality fats while cooking
- Be diversified in food intake

What to do before going on the AIP
How can you address other potential causes of autoimmune disorder before going on the AIP? There are four steps to take before committing to the restrictiveness of the AIP:
Do a basic cleanse of the diet

Most people aren't eating as well as they should, so the first step before considering the AIP is to make some basic improvements to the diet. It may be the step needed to reduce the symptoms, which makes a diet as strict as the AIP unnecessary. What kind of improvements should one make? The first is to eliminate all processed and packaged foods. Eat whole foods or prepackaged foods with a reasonable number of real ingredients. Be especially aware that "health" foods like protein bars or gluten-free meals often contain inflammatory oils and fat. Artificial sweeteners are also a big no-no. Make it a goal to eliminate foods with any added sugar – even raw sugar - but get rid of the artificial stuff first. Alongside the elimination of certain foods, add in fermented foods at least twice a week. This can include kefir, kombucha, and sauerkraut. Be sure to drink lots of water or unsweetened herbal teas, too, since hydration is essential to good health and proper digestion. If these actions don't improve the symptoms, work on avoiding gluten and liquid dairy, as well.

Get tested for food sensitivities
If one has a food sensitivity that's untreated, it can cause leaky gut and lead to an autoimmune condition. Yes, just one food that the body can't tolerate can throw off the entire system and impact the overall health. Consult a doctor about taking what's known as a "delayed IgG sensitivity test." It tests the system for IgG antibodies related to over 90 foods. If any IgG antibodies are present, it means the body is responding to the food like it's a foreign attacker. Then eliminate that specific food or foods from the diet, and the symptoms should go away.

Try gut supplements

One can improve the GI tract using gut supplements, which in turn helps treat an autoimmune condition. If the symptoms aren't too severe, gut supplements like L-glutamine, probiotics, and digestive enzymes can make a big difference. L-glutamine is necessary to keep the body from absorbing harmful bacteria that causes inflammation. Doctors often recommend just five grams per day. High-quality probiotics work to reduce inflammation and improve the immune system. The body needs strong digestive enzymes to break down food and fight bacteria. If your body is not producing enough naturally, then supplements can be taken alongside meals as needed.

Get hormones checked

If your hormones are unbalanced, it can lead to inflammation in the GI tract and autoimmune diseases. The hormones in the thyroid help produce the proper amount of stomach acid, while testosterone strengthens the immune system. If these are low, you can't absorb nutrients as well and the risk for an autoimmune disease goes up. Have your doctor test hormone levels to make sure that isn't the source of the problem. If it isn't, then move forward with the AIP.

AIP-proof foods

a. Variety

For the body to achieve the nutrition needed, embrace variety. You need a variety of plant and animal foods. Different types of foods have different nutrient content. For plants, *eat the rainbow* is a good motto. The plant compounds that act as color pigments also contain nutrients. For instance, carotenoids make vegetables and fruits red, orange, and yellow in color and are used as antioxidants in the body when converted to vitamin A. Chlorophyll is a green pigmentation in plants that can be used for cancer prevention. Every meal should contain two or more vegetables with different colors.

As much as it is good to have different colors, switching to different foods within a given color is also essential. Each plant within a given color has different nutritional value. For instance, collard greens and kale belong to same color of the cruciferous family, but collards have more vitamin B5 and B9, while kale contains more vitamin C and K.

When a variety of vegetables are ingested, there is a reduction in the risk of chronic illness and cancer. Vegetables contain important antioxidants, minerals, phytonutrients, vitamins, and fiber that are beneficial in the fight against autoimmune diseases.

When it comes to animals, the same principle of diversity can be applied. Embrace using different animal sources for meat. For example, ground lamb and ground beef are all red meat, but lamb has more selenium and vitamin B3, while beef contains more zinc and potassium. Furthermore, the nutritional value may vary with the animal parts being used. Organ meat has more nutrients compared to muscle meat. Beef sirloin steak has less vitamin B12 than beef rib-eye steak.

Parts and organs can be purchased separately from the stores or purchase a fraction or whole animal to be cooked in parts. It is also important to embrace different animals from red meat to seafood and shellfish to poultry and more. Seafood and sea vegetables are good sources of essential, long-chain omega-3 polyunsaturated fatty acids.

You can also cook food in a variety of ways. Cooking is known to increase digestibility and bioavailability of some nutrients, while killing some other probiotic organisms and helpful enzymes and de-structuring the fiber. Therefore, some foods can be cooked on high-heat, boiled, fermented, steamed, roasted, slow-cooked, or eaten raw.

b. Gray areas

Some foods are excluded in the AIP plan but are fine for most individuals following a Paleo diet. Such foods include berries and fruit; spices like cardamom, caraway, and pepper; pasture-raised egg yolks; spices extracted from seeds like mustard, cumin, and anise; edible podded legumes like peas, snow peas, snap peas, and green beans; sprouted legumes like mung beans; and nut and seed oils like walnut and macadamia nut oils. Such foods cause problems to individuals with sensitivity, especially when suffering from an autoimmune ailment. Such individuals must eliminate the foods when on AIP and then reintroduce them.

There are nuts and seeds included in this gray area, especially the ones used for preparing herbal teas like cardamom. Others include pseudograins prepared traditionally like buckwheat, fermented kefir, and other varieties of algae, excluding spirulina and chlorella. Wild mushrooms, herbs like turmeric and lemon balm, wine and distilled alcohols are good candidates for this gray area.

c. Origins of food

Most of the foods can be purchased from the standard grocery stores, local farmers (farm stands and farmers' markets), online markets, and specialty stores like health food stores, cultural food markets, natural food stores.

Organic Local Produce – places that offer the required foods. Farmers' markets offer wonderful seasonal produce from organic and conventional farmers. The produce tends to be extremely fresh and flavorful.

Farm stands or fruit stands offer a diversity of freshly picked produce. It is advantageous to live in an area where there are lots of farms and orchards.

Local produce markets specialize in selling an array of regional organic fruits and vegetables.

Organic Meats - Stick with meat that comes from pastured and naturally raised animals. With beef, they are referred to as "grass-fed". With poultry, it is called "free-range". With pork, it is usually referred to as "pastured," and fish is "wild-caught". All of these labels mean that the meats are allowed to graze on the foods they would naturally eat in the wild as opposed to being fed grains in a feed lot.

Organic meats are hormone-free and antibiotic-free. The animals are also fed food that doesn't contain any pesticides, chemicals, antibiotics, or hormones.

d.   Nutrition guidelines

Vegetables – artichoke, green onions, avocado, beets, broccoli, parsnip, brussels sprouts, cabbage, lettuce, carrot, cauliflower, celery, collard greens, cucumber, fennel, kale, chayote, leeks, mushroom, asparagus, onion, okra, pumpkin, salad greens, squash, seaweed, spinach, sweet potato, turnip, zucchini, Swiss chard, watercress

Fruits – blackberries, bananas, blueberries, guava, coconut, dates, grapes, grapefruit, kiwi, lemon, lychees, lime, melon, mangos, oranges, pears, papayas, peaches, pineapple, pomegranate, raspberries, strawberries, watermelon

Meats – beef, chicken, pork, duck, turkey, rabbit, goat, bison, veal, quail, goose, elk, kangaroo, alligator, reindeer, moose, snake, pheasant, organ meats such as kidney, liver, heart, tongue, marrow, and tripe

Herbs and seasonings – garlic, onion powder, basil, bay leaves, ginger, cilantro, parsley, cinnamon, salt, peppermint, oregano, rosemary, thyme, turmeric, sage, horseradish, cloves, lemongrass, chamomile, edible flowers, coconut aminos, apple cider vinegar, balsamic vinegar, white vinegar

Seafood – tuna, red snapper, mackerel, salmon, tilapia, halibut, bass, sole, sardines, grouper, cod, clams, eel, crab, shrimp, anchovies, oysters, scallops, mussels, lobster, eel, mahi mahi, shark, abalone

Fermented food – coconut yogurt, kombucha, kimchi, coconut kefir, sauerkraut

Healthy oils – coconut oil, olive oil, avocado oil, animal fat, lard, grass-fed ghee

Beverages – water, homemade fruit smoothies, and vegetable shakes (omit nightshade vegetables), herbal teas

Other – homemade meat stock, canned coconut milk, coconut cream, honey, maples syrup, gelatin, arrowroot starch, coconut flour

Notes:

- Limit fruit intake to 20 grams per day, especially those with a high content of fructose

- Check coconut products for gluten and other unhealthy chemicals

- Choose vinegars that are sugar-free

- Honey and maple syrup should be used in moderation

Foods & recipes to avoid

Nightshade vegetables and spices – tomato, potato, eggplant, peppers, tomatillos, gooseberries, pepper flakes, cayenne pepper, chili pepper, paprika, garam masala powder, curry powder, hot sauce mixes

Dairy – eggs, mayonnaise, butter, soymilk, animal milk, sweetened condensed milk, ice cream, yogurt, all-purpose cream, cheese

Legumes – red beans, lentils, garbanzo beans, snow peas, black beans, pinto beans, black eyed peas, mongo beans, soybeans, chickpeas, lima beans, kidney beans, tofu

Grains – wheat, rice, sorghum, oats, millet, corn, barley, spelt, buckwheat, rye, kamut

Nuts and seeds – peanuts, quinoa, walnuts, chia seeds, pumpkin seeds, chestnuts, anise seed, cashews, sesame seeds, pecans, sunflower seeds, pistachios, hazelnuts, pine nuts, poppy seed, cumin, mustard seed, nutmeg, annatto seed, coriander, caraway, flax seeds

Processed food – pasta, cookies, pretzels, cakes, pancakes, waffles, chocolate bars, rice cakes, cold cuts, pizza, bread, potato chips, cereals

Beverages – brewed coffee, coffee blends, seed-based organic teas, soda, alcohol, milkshakes, sugar-rich teas, energy drinks

Other – sugars, algae, thickening agents, vegetable oils, seed-based oils, artificial seasonings, food additives, gluten-rich flours, dried fruit, vanilla

Foods prohibited in the AIP diet but that can be reintroduced after 30 days:

Egg yolks – contain the inflammatory soy proteins that will trigger aggravation. Eggs have proteins and enzymes, particular egg whites, that force through to the gut lining when digestion occurs. Soy is commonly used in chicken feed. But egg yolks are also dense with nutrients, so they are often reintroduced first.

Coffee

Nuts and seeds (including oils) - Nuts and seeds are high in anti-nutrients such as lectins and phytates. They are one of the most allergenic types of foods and can cause sensitivities in people struggling with autoimmunity. Reintroduce seeds before nuts, since seeds are easier to digest.

Small doses of gluten-free alcohol

Chocolate

Paprika

Sweet peppers
Eggplant

NSAIDs (Non-Steroidal Anti-Inflammatory Drugs)

NSAIDs are a kind of pain reliever that also bring down fevers and regulate inflammation when prescribed by a doctor. Prolonged use of NSAIDs can lead to stroke, stomach bleeding, and heart attacks. All NSAIDs do not work in a similar manner. All drugs can be aimed at reduction of inflammation and pain, but one NSAID may provide more relief compared to another, and some have fewer side effects.

NSAIDs can also induce renal toxicity and inhibit the functioning of cyclooxygenase (COX) enzymes. Such a blockage may result in asthma, stomach ulcers, stroke, or kidney and liver problems[1].

There are two classes of NSAIDs, the non-selective and selective. Non-selective NSAIDs inhibit both types of COX enzyme and can cause gastric ulceration and alter clotting. Examples are Aspirin, Diclofenac, Naproxen, Piroxican, and Ibuprofen.

Selective NSAIDs block the COX-2 enzyme only, thereby allowing prostaglandin production meant to provide stomach protection and relieve pain, fever, and inflammation. These don't alter clotting. Examples are Celebrex and Mobic[2].

* Avoid the use of NSAIDs like Ibuprofen, Aspirin, and Naproxen. This may seem counterintuitive, as they are designed to reduce inflammation, but they can also cause holes to form in the intestinal lining, which leads to leaky gut syndrome.

---

[1] https://www.ncbi.nlm.nih.gov/pmc/articles/PMC5506195/

[2] https://www.myvmc.com/treatments/nsaids-non-steroidal-anti-inflammatory-drugs/

The AIP pantry

a.   Tips on stocking & storing

Prepare a clipboard and place it near or in the pantry. Write an inventory checklist and attach it to the clipboard and follow it diligently. It is a helpful step in meal planning and prevents buying ingredients in duplicates or running out of things.

When the foods are intended for longer shelf life, store in a dark area that is cool and dry.

Buy the ingredients in bulk. Buy what is required for that period of time and maintain fresh ingredients in the pantry. This is also a good means of saving money.

Buy clear glass containers for storage of the food. Glass material is the best for storage because it is:

- eco-friendly
- airtight
- dishwater-safe
- comparatively cheap
- free harmful petrochemicals that leach and affect stored food

Make use of labels by ensuring ingredients and jars are well labeled. Also include the store date and ensure that the ingredients are rotated, using the oldest in the pantry first.

b.   List of storable AIP foods categorized by how to store them.

Stand-alone freezers
Freezer bags
Refrigerators
Countertops

Lamb, pork, beef, poultry, seafood, bone broth, pate, gelatin gummies – Fridge or freezer

Apples, avocados, berries, broccoli, brussels sprouts, cabbage, carrots, lime, orange, lemon, cauliflower, grapefruit, turnips, cucumber, summer squash, ginger, greens, zucchini, fresh herbs, parsnips, pears - Fridge
Bananas - countertop
Garlic, onions, yams, sweet potatoes, coconut flour, tapioca flour, dry herbs, dried fruits, arrowroot flour, winter squash, baking soda, maple syrup, olive oil, palm oil, avocado oil, coconut oil, spices, honey, vinegar - Pantry

Recipes

Breakfast

Green Piña Colada Smoothie

Ingredients
- 1 c. pineapple
- 1 c. raw kale or spinach
- ½ c. coconut water
- 2 ice cubes
- 1 tbsp. coconut oil
- 1 squeezed lime
- 1 tsp. ginger, ground

Preparation:
1. Add pineapple, coconut water, ginger, and ice cubes to blender. Blend until smooth.
2. Add in the rest of the ingredients and process until smooth.

Triple Berry Smoothie

Ingredients:
- 1 fresh banana
- ½ c. blackberries
- ½ c. raspberries
- ½ c. strawberries
- ½ c. coconut water
- 1 tbsp. coconut oil

Preparation:
1. Add all ingredients to the blender and blend until smooth.

Zesty Grapefruit Bowl

Ingredients

- 1 pink grapefruit, chopped
- 1 chopped avocado
- ½ c. freshly chopped mint
- ½ tbsp. apple cider vinegar
- ½ tbsp. olive oil
- Dash of sea salt

Preparation:

1. Combine all ingredients in a bowl.
2. Serve immediately, or chill overnight.

Tropical Breakfast Salad

Ingredients

- 1 chopped mango
- 1 chopped kiwi
- ¼ c. toasted coconut, shredded
- 2 tbsps. squeezed lime
- 1 tbsp. coconut oil
- ½ tsp. cinnamon, ground
- ½ tsp. ginger, ground

Preparation:

1. Combine mango, kiwi, and coconut in a bowl and mix.
2. Combine lime, coconut oil, and spices in a shaker jar or blender and process until combined.
3. Pour dressing over the salad.

Sweet Potato Breakfast Porridge

Ingredients
- 2 sweet potatoes
- 1 sliced banana
- ½ c. coconut milk
- ¼ c. toasted coconut, shredded
- ½ tsp. cinnamon, ground
- ½ tsp. ginger, ground
- ½ tsp. sea salt

Preparation:
1. Peel and chop the sweet potato. Add to a pot of water, cover, and bring to a boil. Cook until potatoes are soft, then drain the water and return potatoes to the pot.
2. Add banana coconut milk, coconut oil, ginger, and salt, and mash with a potato masher.
3. Serve in bowls topped with toasted coconut.

Apple-Sage Pork Skillet

Ingredients:
- 1 lb. pastured pork, ground
- 1 tbsp. apple cider vinegar
- 1 c. mushroom, diced
- 2 tbsps. freshly minced sage
- ½ c. thinly sliced green onions
- 2 tbsps. coconut oil
- ½ white onion, diced
- 1 white sweet potato, diced
- 1 green apple, diced
- ½ tbsp. sea salt

Preparation:

1. Place fresh coconut oil in the bottom of a heavy-bottomed skillet on medium-high heat. When the fat has melted, add the onion and cook. Stir for few minutes.
2. Reduce heat to medium. Add the sweet potato. Cook for approximately 4 minutes. Stir, adding additional coconut oil if the mixture dries out and begins to stick.
3. Stir in the diced apple and cook for 3 more minutes. Add in the sea salt, sage, and mushrooms, and cook until the sweet potatoes are soft. Turn off the stove, transfer to a medium-sized bowl and set aside.
4. Add the ground pork to the same skillet used for the vegetables. Cook on medium heat until golden brown.
5. Return apple and vegetable mixture to the pan. Stir in the vinegar. Turn off the heat.

Porridge with Lemon and Berries

Ingredients:

- 1 head cauliflower
- Handful mixed berries
- ¼ c. toasted coconut chips
- ¾ c. coconut, shredded
- Spoonful coconut cream, softly whipped
- Zest of 1 lemon
- Salt
- 2 tbsps. coconut butter
- 3 c. coconut milk

Instructions:

1. Slice up the cauliflower into florets and put them into the food processor.
2. Pause for some time until the cauliflower is the same consistency as large grains of rice. Pulse well.
3. Transfer the riced cauliflower to a pan, then add the remaining porridge ingredients and stir.
4. Bring up to a simmer, cover with a lid and cook for close to 30 minutes until the cauliflower is tender and the porridge nice.
5. Whip the coconut cream while the porridge is cooling. Start by removing the chilled coconut milk from the fridge.
6. Pour the thin coconut water into a jar.
7. Scoop out the cream and heat with a balloon whisk until soft peaks form.

Turkey Sausage

Ingredients:

- 1 lb. turkey, ground
- 1 tsp. sea salt
- 1 tsp. rosemary, fresh
- 1 tsp. thyme, fresh
- 2 tbsps. coconut oil
- ½ tsp. garlic powder
- ½ tsp. cinnamon
- 2 tsps. Sage, fresh

Preparation:

1. Combine all ingredients except the oil and refrigerate for at least 30 minutes.
2. Add the oil and shape into patties. Cook in a lightly oiled skillet over medium heat until no longer pink in the middle.
3. Bake at 400°F for 25 minutes alternatively.
4. Serve hot.

Risotto with Greens

Ingredients:

- 1 lb. cubed butternut squash, peeled
- 1 tsp. oregano, dried
- ½ tsp. onion powder
- ¼ tsp. cinnamon
- ¼ tsp. turmeric
- 1 tbsp. solid cooking fat
- 1 clove minced garlic
- 1 bunch rainbow chard
- 1 tsp. sea salt

Preparation:
1. Place squash in food processor and pulse for 45 seconds until squash is riced.
2. Heat solid cooking fat in a large skillet on medium-low heat. Add squash when fat has melted.
3. Cook and stir occasionally for 4-5 minutes. Add garlic, cook until fragrant.
4. Add remaining spices. Stir and cook 4-5 more minutes.
5. Add chard and cook for 2 minutes while covered, until chard wilts.
6. Serve warm.

Italian Spiced 50/50 Sausages

Ingredients:
- 1 lb. ground beef, grass-fed
- ½ tsp. sea salt
- 1 tbsp. fresh thyme, minced
- 1 tbsp. coconut oil
- ½ tsp. garlic powder
- 1 lb. ground pork, pastured
- 1 tbsp. fresh oregano, minced

Preparation:
1. Place the ground beef, pork, herbs, garlic powder, and salt in a large bowl and combine well with hands. Form into 7 or more patties and place on a plate.
2. Heat the solid cooking fat in a frying pan on medium heat. Add patties when the fat is melted. Cook thoroughly. Can be done in two batches.

Plantain Wrap

Ingredients:
- 3 green plantains
- 1/3 c. extra virgin olive oil
- 1 tsp. sea salt
- 1 c. water

Preparation:
1. Peel and chop green plantains.
2. Puree the plantains in the food processor.
3. Add the remaining ingredients and puree for a minute or two.
4. Scrape the sides of the processor so any larger chunks get incorporated.
5. Spread onto a parchment-lined sheet tray.
6. Bake at 375 degrees F for about 25-30 minutes.
7. Cut into 6 pieces and serve.

Banana Bread

Ingredients:

- 1 c. ripe bananas, mashed
- ½ tsp. baking soda
- 1 tbsp. honey
- 1 tsp. vanilla
- 1½ tsps. lemon juice
- ¼ c. coconut flour
- ½ c. arrowroot starch
- ½ tsp. salt
- ½ tsp. cinnamon
- ¼ c. coconut oil, melted
- ½ c. coconut butter softened

Preparation:

1. Preheat oven to 350 degrees F.
2. Grease pan with coconut oil.
3. Mix wet ingredients in mixer until smooth.
4. Mix dry ingredients together in a bowl.
5. Combine the dry mixture with the wet ingredients.
6. Spread into prepared pan.
7. Bake for 25-30 minutes.

Savory Breakfast Cookies

Ingredients:
- ½ c. coconut flour
- 4 tbsps. extra-virgin olive oil
- ½ tbsp. raw apple cider vinegar
- ½ tsp. baking soda
- 1 tsp. garlic, dried granulated
- 6 tbsps. coconut oil
- 1 tsp. rosemary, dried
- 4 tbsps. gelatin
- ½ tsp. unrefined salt
- 1 c. filtered water

Preparation:
1. Preheat oven to 350°F (177°C).
2. "Bloom" and melt the gelatin to get it ready to use. In a small pot, add water and drizzle the top with gelatin, half a tablespoon at a time in each layer. Do not pour it all in one area or let it clump. Spread it evenly to avoid clumps. Stir thoroughly after adding and wetting every half tablespoon. When all gelatin is wet, heat for some minutes over medium low till all gelatin melts. Keep stirring occasionally until it dissolves.
3. In a bowl, mix all the dry ingredients.
4. Add the wet ingredients to the gelatin after it is dissolved. In the bowl with the dry ingredients, add the wet ingredients and use a big spoon to stir to form batter.
5. Line a baking sheet with a parchment paper. Divide the batter using a spoon into 12 cookies. Bake in the oven until cookies are golden brown, about 40-45 minutes.

Banana-Pumpkin Breakfast Smoothie Bowl

Ingredients:
- 2 sliced ripe bananas
- ½ tsp. ground cinnamon
- ½ c. coconut milk, full-fat
- 1 tbsp. gelatin powder
- 1 tsp. honey
- 6 tbsps. pumpkin puree
- Toasted coconut flakes and fresh fruit

Preparation:
1. Blend together cinnamon, honey, gelatin powder, coconut milk, pumpkin puree, and bananas on high until smooth, for about 20-30 seconds.
2. Pour into a bowl and use toasted cornflakes and fresh fruit to garnish.

Baked Breakfast Casserole with Apples and Raisins

Ingredients:
- 1 c. ripe mashed plantain
- 4 c. cooked spaghetti squash flesh
- ½ c. raisins
- ¼ tsp. mace, ground
- ½ c. applesauce
- 2 tbsps. tapioca starch
- ½ tsp. sea salt
- 1 peeled and diced apple
- ½ tsp. baking soda
- 1 tsp. vanilla extract
- ¼ c. avocado oil
- 2 tablespoons gelatin powder
- 1½ tsps. Cinnamon, ground
- 1 tsp. cream of tartar

Preparation:
1. The night before: combine raisins, diced apple, avocado oil, vanilla extract, seas salt, applesauce, ground mace, ground cinnamon, mashed plantain, and spaghetti squash in a large bowl. Refrigerate overnight, covered.
2. Combine cream of tartar, baking soda, tapioca starch, and gelatin powder in a smaller bowl. Cover the mixture and place it on countertop.
3. The following morning: Preheat oven to 350°F. (175°C) Get the spaghetti mixture from the fridge and stir in the dry ingredients to combine. Lightly grease a glass casserole dish. Scoop mixture into the casserole dish and evenly spread, using a fork to form line patterns.
4. Line the casserole dish with a foil sheet to catch drips that may drip when baking. Bake for 60 minutes, or until bubbly on the edges and lightly browned. Serve warm or wait for it to cool.

Turkey Apple Breakfast Hash

Ingredients:

- 1 lb. ground turkey
- ½ tsp. cinnamon
- ½ tsp. thyme, dried
- 1 tbsp. coconut oil
- 1 onion
- ½ c. shredded carrots
- 2 c. cubed frozen butternut squash
- 1 tbsp. coconut oil
- 2 c. spinach
- 1 tsp. cinnamon
- 1 large zucchini
- 1 peeled and chopped apple, cored
- ½ tsp. turmeric
- ¾ tsp. powdered ginger
- ½ tsp. garlic powder
- Sea salt

Ingredients:

1. In a skillet heat 1 tablespoon of coconut oil. Add turkey cook until color changes to brown. Add sea salt, thyme, and cinnamon to season. Transfer to a plate.
2. Using the coconut oil that remains in the skillet, add onions and sauté until soft, or about 2-3 minutes.
3. Add frozen squash, apple, carrots, and zucchini and cook until the vegetables are soft, about 4-5 minutes.
4. Add the spinach and stir for 2-3 minutes.
5. Stir in salt, seasonings, and turkey and turn the heat off.
6. Enjoy while warm or refrigerate for later serving.

Biscuits

Ingredients:
- ¾ c. coconut flour
- ¼ c. olive oil
- 1 c. tapioca starch
- ½ tsp. sea salt
- 1 tsp. gelatin
- 1 tsp. cream of tartar
- 1 tsp. baking soda
- ¾ c. canned full fat coconut milk

Preparation:
1. Set oven to 375°F (191°C) and place a parchment paper on a baking sheet.
2. Combine gelatin, cream of tartar, baking soda, tapioca starch, coconut flour, and sea salt in a medium bowl until combined well.
3. Mix coconut milk and olive oil in a measuring cup until well combined to form a soft dough.
4. Combine the dry and wet ingredients.
5. Scoop the dough onto the parchment paper using a ¼ cup measuring cup. Pat to get firmer, flatter biscuits.
6. Bake for about 15-20 minutes, or until golden brown. Allow some minutes to cool while still on the baking sheet.

Raisin Bran

Ingredients:
- 2 c. thick coconut flakes
- 1 tsp. cinnamon
- 1/3 c. raisins

Preparation:
1. Preheat oven to 325°F (163°C).
2. On a cookie sheet, spread the flakes and evenly drizzle cinnamon on top.
3. Put in oven for 5 minutes and mix the coconut midway to toast evenly until golden brown. Let cool.
4. Move coconut to a sealed bag, container, or jar and add the raisins.
5. Serve in bowl with additive-free coconut milk.

Tostones and Ground Turkey Breakfast Patties

Ingredients
For turkey patties:
- 1 package lean turkey, ground
- 1 chopped apple
- ½ minced onion
- ½ c. chopped dates
- ½ tsp. cinnamon
- ½ tsp. turmeric
- 1 tsp. honey

For Tostones:
- 2 plantains with yellow or slightly black skin
- 1 tbsp. coconut oil

Preparation:
1. Preheat oven to 350 degrees F. In a bowl, mix the ground turkey and remaining ingredients together. Form bite-sized patties and place in oven. Bake 15-20 minutes.
2. While patties are baking, preheat a pan with coconut oil. Chop plantains in 1-inch pieces. Fry each piece 2 minutes on each side. Remove from pan and place individually between parchment paper. /smash pieces down with a can and place back in pan for 2 min each side. Serve with turkey patties.

Breakfast Cookies

Ingredients:

- 1 large mashed yam, cooked
- 1 banana
- ½ c. coconut flakes, unsweetened
- ½ c. coconut flour
- Handful chopped dates
- Carob chips
- ½ tsp. cinnamon
- 1 tbsp. honey

Preparation:

1. Preheat oven to 350F. Mix all ingredients together and form into cookies. Make 4 huge cookies and bake for 20 minutes. Serve with fruit and honey on top for a healthy sweet treat!

AIP Tapioca Breakfast Pudding

Ingredients:

- 4 tbsps. tapioca
- 1 tbsp. honey
- ½ tsp. cinnamon
- 1 can full-fat, guar gum-free coconut milk
- ½ c. water

Preparation:

1. Add all the ingredients in a pot. Whisk until bubbling and add the flour. Whisk until mixed together and pour in bowls. Add whatever topping desired.

Lunch

Chilled Cucumber Avocado Soup

Ingredients
- 2 English cucumbers
- 1 chopped ripe avocado
- ½ c. cilantro, fresh
- 1 c. water, filtered
- 2 tbsps. squeezed lime
- 1 tsp. sea salt

Preparation:
1. Roughly chop cucumber and add it to a blender with the cilantro and water. Process until smooth.
2. Add the rest of the ingredients and process until smooth.
3. Refrigerate for at least 30 minutes or until ready to serve.
4.

Creamy Butternut Squash Soup

Ingredients
- 1 chopped yellow onion
- 4 c. chopped butternut squash
- 2 chopped apples
- 2 tbsps. apple cider vinegar
- 4 c. water
- 1 tsp. cinnamon, ground
- 1 tsp. ginger, ground
- 1 tsp. turmeric
- 1 tsp. sea salt

Preparation:
1. Sauté onions in olive oil in a large stockpot over medium-high heat until translucent.
2. Add squash and sauté about 5 minutes
3. Add apples, vinegar, water, and spices.
4. Cover and bring to a boil.
5. Reduce heat to medium and simmer for approximately 30 minutes, until squash is tender.
6. Using a blender, puree the soup.

Gingery Carrot Beet Soup

Ingredients
- 1 chopped yellow onion
- 3 lbs. chopped carrots
- 2 chopped large beets
- 2 inches freshly chopped ginger
- 2 c. chicken broth
- 2 c. water
- 2 tbsps. coconut oil
- 1 tsp. sea salt

Preparation:
1. Sauté onions in coconut oil in a large stockpot over medium-high heat until translucent.
2. Add carrots, beets, and ginger, and sauté about 5 minutes
3. Add broth, water, and spices.
4. Cover and bring to a boil.
5. Reduce heat to medium and simmer for approximately 30 minutes, until vegetables are tender.
6. Using a blender, puree the soup.

Shrimp "Tacos"

Ingredients:
- 12 clean jumbo shrimp
- 4 lettuce leaves, washed and dried
- 1 chopped avocado
- 1 tbsp. olive oil
- 1 c. grated jicama
- ½ c. freshly chopped cilantro
- 1 lime, chopped into 4 pieces
- Sea salt

Preparation:
1. Sauté the shrimp in olive oil until opaque on both sides.
2. Put 2 lettuce leaves on each of 2 serving plates.
3. Spoon 3 shrimp onto each of the lettuce leaves.
4. Top each with jicama, avocado, and cilantro.
5. Squeeze lime over each lettuce taco and salt to taste.

Cucumber "Sushi"

Ingredients:
- 4 sheets of nori
- 2 mashed avocados
- 8 oz. salmon, smoked
- 1 cucumber
- 1 carrot
- ½ c. watercress
- Daikon radish

Preparation:
1. Cut cucumber, carrot, and daikon into long thin strips.
2. Cut salmon into long, thin strips.
3. Place nori sheet flat on a hard surface, with the shiny side facing down.
4. Spread 1/4 of the mashed avocado evenly over the nori.

5. Place 1/4 of the salmon and vegetables in a long strip in the middle of the piece of nori.
6. Roll the nori tightly from one end to the other, using the avocado to help it "stick."
7. Repeat with the other 3 sheets.
8. Chill for about 30 minutes.
9. Cut the rolls into pieces with a sharp knife and serve.

Summer Rolls with Mango Dipping Sauce

Ingredients:
- 4 lettuce leaves, washed and dried
- 8 oz. shredded chicken, cooked
- 1 peeled cucumber
- ¼ c. cilantro, fresh
- ¼ c. mint, fresh
- ¼ c. basil, fresh
- 1 chopped mango
- 2 tbsps. apple cider vinegar
- 2 tbsps. water, filtered
- 1 tbsp. olive oil
- 1 tsp. ginger, ground
- ½ tsp. sea salt

Preparation:
1. Blend the mango, vinegar, water, oil, ginger, and salt in a blender until smooth. Serve in small bowls for dipping.
2. Put 2 lettuce leaves on each of 2 serving plates.
3. Divide the chicken, cucumber, and herbs between each of the 4 lettuce leaves.
4. Wrap each roll like a burrito, rolling one inch of the top down and one inch of the bottom up. Then roll from left to right.
5. Serve with mango dipping sauce.

Nicoise Salad

Ingredients:
- 2 cans albacore tuna
- 2 c. Boston lettuce
- 1 thinly sliced red onion
- 1 c. sliced radishes
- 1 c. green string beans
- ¼ c. kalamata olives
- 2 tbsps. capers
- 2 tbsps. olive oil
- 2 tbsps. lemon juice
- ½ tsp. thyme, dried
- ½ tsp. basil, dried
- ½ tsp. oregano, dried
- Sea salt

Preparation:
1. Trim green beans and steam in about ½ inch water until bright green. Insert beans in a bowl containing ice water.
2. Wash, dry, and tear the lettuce into bite-sized pieces. Divide between 2 serving plates.
3. Arrange the green beans, onion, radishes, olives, and tuna on the beds of lettuce.
4. In a separate bowl, whisk the oil, lemon juice, and spices.
5. Pour dressing over the salads and apply a topping of capers. Add salt to taste.

Strawberry Salmon Salad

Ingredients:
- 12 oz. wild salmon fillets
- 2 c. mixed salad greens
- 1 c. sliced strawberries
- 1 peeled and cubed avocado
- 2 tbsps. olive oil
- 2 tbsps. balsamic vinegar, unsweetened

- 1 tbsp. lemon juice
- Sea salt

Preparation:
1. Place salmon in a deep-sided sauté pan. Add 1/2-inch water and lemon juice to the pan. Cover and cook over medium high heat until fish is cooked through (8-10 minutes depending on thickness).
2. Divide the salad greens between 2 serving plates.
3. Arrange salmon, strawberries, and avocado on the lettuce.
4. In a bowl, whisk the oil and vinegar with the salt.
5. Pour the dressing over the salads.

Cranberry Apple Coleslaw

Ingredients:
- ½ thinly sliced red cabbage
- ½ thinly sliced green cabbage
- 2 tbsps. extra-virgin olive oil
- ½ tsp. white wine vinegar
- ¼ tsp. sea salt
- 1 peeled and cored apple, diced
- ½ c. fresh cranberries

Preparation:
1. In a serving bowl, add in the sliced cabbages.
2. In a separate bowl, mix vinegar, olive oil, and salt. Pour over the bowl containing cabbage mixture and toss well to coat.
3. Toss in cranberries and apple. Serve immediately or refrigerate for a maximum of 4 days.

Tuna Salad with Plantain Chips

Ingredients:
- Canned tuna drained
- 1 head romaine lettuce
- 1½ diced avocado
- 1 diced green onion

- 1 diced apple
- A few chopped black olives
- ½ chopped cucumber
- Handful chopped dates
- ½ lemon
- 1 lime
- Handful chopped romaine
- Store bought plantain chips (made with coconut oil, preferably)

Preparation:
1. Super-fast and easy to make! Mix all the ingredients together and squeeze in the lemon and lime. Scoop on top of romaine and add some plantain chips on the side. This is awesome for a nice light dinner on a hot evenin

Chicken Salad with Blueberries, Beets and Avocado

Ingredients:
- 1 roasted chicken, store bought
- 1 head romaine lettuce
- 1 c. blueberries
- Handful sliced beets, canned
- ¼ onions, sliced
- 1 avocado
- Balsamic and coconut oil for dressing

Preparation:
Chop lettuce and place on two plates. Pull chicken into shreds and distribute onto lettuce. Add blueberries and half an avocado on both plates. Add as much onion as desired and top with dressing.

Shrimp Ceviche

Ingredients:
- 1½ c. cucumber, seeded and chopped
- 1½ c. green apple, chopped
- Flesh of 1 avocado, diced
- 1 c. cooked shrimp, chopped
- ¼ c. parsley, chopped
- 2 tbsps. finely chopped mint
- 2 tbsps. olive oil
- 2 tbsps. lemon juice
- ½ tsp. sea salt
- ¼ tsp. garlic powder

Preparation:
1. In a serving bowl, place in all ingredients and combine. Refrigerate for at least two hours to let flavors blend together. Stir well before serving.

Ground Turkey Cauliflower Rice Bowl

Ingredients:
- 1 head cauliflower
- 2 tbsps. coconut oil
- 1 package ground turkey
- ½ diced onion
- 1 diced apple
- 2-4 tbsps. coconut aminos
- ¼ tsp. sea salt together with other spices to taste
- 1 diced avocado

Preparation:
1. Use a food processor to chop up cauliflower until it resembles rice.
2. Heat up a frying pan with 2 tbsps. coconut oil and add cauliflower, mix around until it browns. Can take up to 20 minutes. Meanwhile, pan fry ground turkey. Add onions and apples half way through.

3. When turkey is done, add sea salt and desired spices and 2-4 tbsps. coconut aminos (tastes like soy sauce), depending on how much flavor is desired. When cauliflower is done, serve in bowls and add ground turkey and diced avocado on top.

Dinner

Shrimp Scampi Spaghetti Squash

Ingredients

- 1 spaghetti squash, halved lengthwise and deseeded
- ½ lb. clean shrimp
- 4 minced cloves garlic
- 3 tbsps. olive oil, plus 1 tsp.
- ½ c. freshly chopped parsley
- 1 tsp. sea salt

Preparation:
1. Preheat oven to 400 degrees F.
2. Place cut-side down of the squash on a cookie sheet lightly coated with 1 teaspoon of olive oil. Pierce the skin several times with a fork.
3. Bake spaghetti squash for approximately 30 minutes, until a fork goes through the skin easily.
4. While the squash bakes, sauté the garlic in 2 tbsps. of olive oil for 1 minute.
5. Add the shrimp to the sauté pan and cook until opaque and pink. Set aside.
6. When the spaghetti squash is done and cool enough to handle, scrape out the strands with a fork into a large bowl.
7. Toss the spaghetti squash strands with the remaining 1 tbsp. of olive oil, the parsley, and the sea salt.
8. Serve spaghetti on plates topped with the sautéed shrimp mixture.

Cod with Basil Pesto

Ingredients:

- 1 lb. fresh cod fillets
- 2 c. basil, fresh
- ¼ c. shredded coconut, unsweetened
- 2 tbsps. lemon juice
- ¼ c. olive oil, and an extra 1 tbsp.

- 1 clove garlic
- 1 tsp. sea salt
- Lemon wedges

Preparation:
1. Preheat oven to 400 degrees F.
2. Lightly coat a baking sheet with part of the 1 tbsp. of oil. Place the fish on the pan and pour the remainder of the 1 tbsp. of oil over the fish.
3. Bake for 20 minutes, until opaque.
4. While fish is baking, combine basil, coconut, lemon juice, olive oil, garlic, and salt in a food processor and process 30-45 seconds, until combined but still coarse.
5. Serve cod topped with pesto.

Halibut with Olive Tapenade

Ingredients:
- 1 lb. halibut fillets, fresh
- 1 jar drained kalamata olives
- 1 jar drained green olives
- ¼ c. olive oil, plus 1 tbsp. more
- 1 tbsp. lemon juice
- 1 clove garlic
- ½ tsp. sea salt

Preparation:
1. Preheat oven to 400 °F.
2. Lightly coat a baking sheet with part of the 1 tbsp. of oil. Place the fish on the pan and pour the remainder of the 1 tbsp. of oil over the fish.
3. Bake for 20-30 minutes, until opaque.
4. While fish is baking, combine olives, olive oil, lemon juice, garlic, and salt in a food processor and process 30-45 seconds, until coarsely chopped.
5. Serve halibut topped with tapenade.
6. Serve with a green vegetable, such as sautéed spinach.

Coconut Chicken Stir Fry

Ingredients:
- 1 lb. chicken meat
- 1 sliced yellow onion
- 1 lb. chopped broccoli
- 4 tbsps. coconut oil
- 4 chopped cloves garlic
- 1 tbsp. ginger, grated
- 1 orange
- 1 tsp. sea salt

Preparation:
1. Sauté onions in coconut oil in a deep sauté pan or wok for about 3 minutes, or until translucent.
2. Stir in the chicken and cook until lightly browned.
3. Add the broccoli and continue to sauté for a few minutes.
4. In a separate bowl, mix the juice from 1 orange, the garlic, ginger, and salt, and whisk until blended.
5. Pour the sauce over the chicken and broccoli and cover until the broccoli is tender.

Roasted Chicken with Root Vegetables

Ingredients:
- 4 large chicken breast halves, bone-in and skin-on
- 6 tbsps. olive oil
- 3 tbsps. apple cider vinegar
- 1 quartered yellow onion
- 4 chopped parsnips
- 2 sliced stalks celery
- 2 c. baby carrots
- 2 c. halved mushrooms
- 4 minced garlic cloves

- 2 tbsps. fresh rosemary
- 1 tsp. sea salt

Preparation:
1. Preheat oven to 400 °F.
2. In a large skillet, warm 1 tbsp. of oil and brown chicken for about 8 minutes per side.
3. In a large roasting pan, toss the vegetables with 2 tbsp. of the oil.
4. In a separate bowl, mix the apple cider vinegar with the remaining 3 tbsp. of oil, garlic, salt, and rosemary.
5. Lay the browned chicken breasts on top of the vegetables. Pour the sauce over the chicken and vegetables.
6. Bake for 35-40 minutes until chicken is cooked through and vegetables are tender.

Turkey Burgers with Fries

Ingredients:
- 4 medium sweet potatoes, peeled and sliced
- 3 tbsps. olive oil
- 1 lb. ground turkey
- 1 diced red onion
- ½ c. fresh parsley
- 2 minced garlic cloves
- 2 tsps. sea salt
- ½ tsp. cinnamon

Preparation:
1. Preheat the oven to 450 °F.
2. In a bowl, mix olive oil, 1 tsp. of salt, and cinnamon and toss in the sweet potatoes.
3. Bake in a single layer on a baking sheet for about 25-30 minutes, turning once.
4. While the fries are cooking, mix turkey, onion, parsley, garlic, and 1 tsp. salt together and form into 4 large patties.
5. Grill on an outdoor grill or pan fry for 7 minutes per side.

Slow-Cooked Pulled Pork and Cabbage

Ingredients:
- 2 lbs. pork roast
- 1 sliced onion
- 4 sliced apples
- 4 c. shredded red cabbage
- ½ c. water
- 2 tbsps. apple cider vinegar
- 1 tsp. cinnamon
- 1 tsp. sea salt

Preparation:
1. Add water, apples, cabbage, onion, and vinegar to slow cooker and stir to combine.
2. Rub salt on the roast, then add it to the crockpot.
3. Cook for 8-10 hours on low.
4. Before serving, shred the pork using 2 forks.
5. Scoop the cabbage-apple mixture onto plates and top with the pulled pork

Slow-Cooked Beef Stew

Ingredients:
- 3 lbs. beef stew meat
- 1 yellow onion
- 4 carrots
- 2 peeled sweet potatoes
- 2 peeled parsnips
- 2 peeled turnips
- 2 minced garlic cloves
- 2 c. beef broth
- 1 bay leaf
- 1 tsp. thyme
- 1 tsp. sea salt

Preparation:
1. Add the broth to a slow cooker.
2. Chop the beef into 1-inch chunks (if not already pre-cut) and add to the slow cooker.
3. Add the spices and salt to the slow cooker.
4. Chop the vegetables into 1/2- to 1-inch pieces and add to the slow cooker.
5. Cover and cook on low heat for at least 8 hours.

Shepherd's Pie

Ingredients:
- 2 lbs. ground beef
- 1 chopped onion
- 2 chopped celery stalks
- 2 chopped carrots
- 1 c. chopped mushrooms
- 4 minced garlic cloves

- 1 tbsp. rosemary
- 1 head cauliflower
- 2 tbsps. olive oil
- 1 tsp. sea salt

Preparation:
1. Brown the meat with the onion, celery, carrots, mushrooms, and garlic in a large stockpot. Cook until meat is fully cooked, about 15-20 minutes
2. In another stockpot, steam cauliflower for about 20 minutes.
3. Preheat oven to 400 °F.
4. Drain the cauliflower and return it to the pot. Mash it with a potato masher. Mix in the olive oil and sea salt.
5. Transfer the beef mixture to a large casserole pan and pat down with a spatula.
6. Spread the mashed cauliflower over the top of the meat.
7. Bake for 40 minutes, until cauliflower starts to brown.

Broiled Lamb Chops with Slaw

Ingredients:
- 4 lamb chops
- 4 minced garlic cloves
- 2 tbsps. fresh rosemary
- 2 tbsps. olive oil
- 1 tsp. sea salt
- 2 peeled beets
- 4 peeled carrots
- 1 apple
- 2 tbsps. apple cider vinegar

Preparation:
1. In a bowl, rub chops with olive oil, salt, garlic, and rosemary.
2. Broil for 10-12 minutes (until medium rare)
3. Grate the carrots, beets, and apple and place in a large bowl. Toss with the vinegar.
4. Serve the slaw alongside the lamb.

Lemon and Herb Salmon with Mashed Coconut Sweet Potato

Ingredients:
Salmon Ingredients:
(Make ahead and marinate for full flavor)
- 2 wild salmon fillets
- Juice from 1 lemon
- 1-2 tbsps. fresh dill
- ½ tsp. thyme, dried
- ½ tsp. rosemary, dried
- ½ tsp. sea salt

Mashed sweet potato ingredients:
- 2 large boiled and mashed sweet potatoes
- ½ c. full-fat, guar gum-free, canned coconut milk
- 1 tbsp. coconut oil
- 1 tsp. sea salt

Preparation:
1. Preheat oven to 350F.
2. Place marinated salmon on a lined baking sheet and bake 15-20 minutes. Do not overcook!
3. Meanwhile boil and mash sweet potato and add all the rest of the ingredients with desired amount of coconut milk and sea salt.
4. Serve salmon and mashed sweet potato together immediately.

AIP Yam and Broccoli Soup

Ingredients:
- 3 cubed yams
- 1 chopped broccoli head
- ½ onion

- 1 box vegetable broth (no yeast, no msg, no guar gum)
- 1 tbsp. thyme and basil
- 1 can full-fat coconut milk

Preparation:
1. Boil all ingredients together until yams are soft, about 20 minutes.
2. Take off the burner and cool slightly before blending.
3. Blend or use a Braun hand mixer, then add coconut milk and blend.

AIP Mushroom Soup

Ingredients:
- 2 tbsps. olive oil
- ½ chopped onion
- 4 chopped Portobello mushrooms
- 2 c. chicken broth or vegetable broth (avoid msg, yeast extract, guar gum or other weird additives)

- ¾ c. canned coconut milk
- ¼ tsp. salt

Preparation:
1. Pan fry the olive oil and onions in a large pot until the onions are soft, 5-7 minutes.
2. Throw in the mushrooms and pan fry for another 5 minutes until soft. Pour in broth and coconut cream and boil for 15 minutes.
3. After 15 minutes, blend the soup until thick. If too thick, add some more broth. If it's too runny mix some arrowroot powder in a bit of water and blend in with the soup.
4. Serve and add parsley for garnish (just to look fancy).

AIP Butternut Squash Soup

Ingredients:
- 2 butternut squash, peeled and cubed
- 3 carrots
- 2 c. vegetable broth
- 1 tbsp. thyme, dried
- 1 tbsp. oregano, dried

Preparation:
1. Boil all ingredients together until soft.
2. Cool slightly and blend with a Braun hand mixer or in a blender. Add a whole can of coconut milk, mostly the fat. Mix until blended.

Snacks and Side Dishes

Red and Green Apple Cinnamon Crisps

Ingredients:
- 2 Granny Smith apples
- 2 red apples
- 1 tsp. cinnamon
- ½ tsp. sea salt

Preparation:
1. Preheat oven to 200 °F.
2. Line 2 baking sheets with parchment paper.
3. Slice the apples thinly into rounds or half-rounds.
4. Lay the apples on the baking sheets in a single layer, and sprinkle with cinnamon and salt.
5. Bake for 1 hour.
6. Take the chips out and turn them over. Bake for 1 more hour until fully done.

Baked Kale Chips

Ingredients:
- 1 bunch of kale
- 1 tbsp. olive oil
- ½ tsp. onion powder
- ½ tsp. garlic powder
- 1 tsp. sea salt

Preparation:
1. Preheat oven to 300 °F.
2. Line 2 baking sheets with parchment paper.
3. Remove stems from kale and tear it into pieces. Place the kale into a large bowl.

4. Add the olive oil, and "massage" it into the kale with hands.
5. Spread the kale evenly between the 2 baking sheets. Sprinkle with the spices.
6. Bake for 15 minutes, then rotate the pans, placing the top pan on the bottom and the bottom pan on the top.
7. Bake for another 15 minutes.

Coconut Ice Cream

Ingredients:
- 2 cans full-fat coconut milk
- 1 banana, frozen
- 2 pitted dates
- 4 ice cubes
- ½ tsp. cinnamon

Preparation:
1. Remove the coconut milk from refrigerator. Flip cans over and open from the bottom. Pour off the liquid into a separate bowl.
2. Add the thick coconut "cream" from the cans to a blender.
3. Add the frozen banana, the cinnamon, the ice, and the dates (if using)
4. Blend until thick and creamy.

5. Eat instantly or set in the freezer for 15-30 minutes for a harder texture.

Tigernut Cheese Cracker

Ingredients:
- 1 c. tigernut flour
- 1 tbsp. gelatine
- ½ tsp. turmeric powder
- 1 tsp. sea salt
- ¼ c. water
- 1 tbsp. nutritional yeast
- 3 tbsps. coconut oil
- ½ tsp. black pepper

Preparation:
1. Set oven to 350°F. Using a mixing bowl, mix the tigernut flour, nutritional yeast, salt, turmeric, and coconut oil and set aside.
2. Pour ¼ cup of water into a small saucepan and add to a stove top. Slowly sprinkle the gelatin into the water and allow it to bloom for 1-2 minutes. Turn the heat on for 2-3 minutes to allow the gelatin to melt. Take from heat and thoroughly mix until it foams.
3. Pour the gelatin egg into the dough and stir quickly to combine.
4. Line a parchment paper to a baking sheet and set the dough on the paper. Cover with another parchment paper.
5. Flatten the dough until even and thin.
6. Using a knife, slice the dough into crackers.
7. Bake crackers until crispy for 8-12 minutes. Let cool before using a spatula to remove from the pan.
8. Serve immediately or store in the fridge.

Asian Stuffed Mushrooms

Ingredients:
- 20 white button mushrooms
- ½ lb. ground chicken
- 2 green onions, finely chopped
- 6 minced cloves garlic
- 1 tbsp. minced ginger
- 1 tsp. salt
- 4 tbsps. coconut aminos
- ½ tsp. apple cider vinegar

Preparation:
1. Combine the ground chicken, green onions, ginger, garlic, coconut aminos, and salt in a mixing bowl and mix well
2. Clean the mushrooms. Using the hands stuff the meat mixture into the mushrooms.
3. Either bake or steam these.
4. Mix the garlic, coconut aminos, and vinegar in a small bowl together to make the dipping sauce.
5. Serve the steamed stuffed mushrooms with the dipping sauce.

Salmon Cakes

Ingredients:
- 10 oz. salmon
- 1 tbsp. freshly chopped dill
- 28g c. coconut flour
- 32g arrowroot flour
- ¼ c. coconut oil
- Salt

Preparation:
1. Preheat oven to 350 degrees F.
2. In a mixing bowl, combine all ingredients.

3. Line a baking tray with parchment paper.
4. Form the mixture into small flat cakes.
5. Arrange on the tray and bake for 25-30 minutes.
6. Let cool.
7. Serve alongside a light salad and coconut cream.

Pumpkin Granola

Ingredients:
- 1 tbsp. pumpkin puree
- 2 tbsps. melted coconut oil
- 1 tbsp. maple syrup
- 2 tsps. cinnamon
- ½ tsp. sea salt

Preparation:
1. Preheat the oven to 350 degrees F and line a baking sheet with parchment paper.
2. Into a large bowl, pour all dry ingredients and mix.
3. Add in the pumpkin puree, maple syrup, coconut oil and stir to evenly coat.
4. Spoon the mixture out onto the baking sheet and bake for about 10-12 minutes.
5. Keep a close eye on the granola to ensure it doesn't burn.
6. Take out from the oven and let cool.
7. Refrigerate for 5-7 days and serve as a snack.

Sardine & Avocado on Endives

Ingredients:
- 2 bunches endives
- 1 tin sardines in olive oil
- 1 tbsp. apple cider vinegar
- 1 tbsp. lemon juice

- 2 tbsps. fresh parsley
- 1 chopped avocado
- ½ tsp. sea salt

Preparation:
1. In a medium bowl, combine the sardines, vinegar, parsley, and lemon juice. Marinate the sardines for about 30 minutes in the refrigerator.
2. In the meantime, remove the leaves from the endives, wash them, and pat them dry. Set them on a platter, with the "cup" side facing up.
3. After the sardines are chilled, mix in the avocados. Divide mixture among the endive leaves using a spoon. There should be enough mixture to fill about 12 leaves.

Smoked Salmon Bites

Ingredients:
- 1 cucumber
- 4 oz. smoked salmon
- 1 avocado
- ½ red onion
- 1 tbsp. lemon juice
- ½ tsp. sea salt
- Chives

Preparation:
1. Slice the cucumber into ¾-inch thick slices.
2. Slice the smoked salmon into 1-inch by 1-inch pieces.
3. In a bowl, mash together the avocado with salt, lemon juice, and onion.
4. Spread the avocado mash evenly across each of the cucumber slices.
5. Top each cucumber with a piece of the smoked salmon.
6. Garnish with a chive, if desired.

Carrot Dip with Crudités

Ingredients:
- 1 lb. carrots
- 2 tbsps. coconut oil
- 1 minced clove garlic
- 1 tsp. minced ginger
- ½ tsp. sea salt
- 1 tbsp. lemon juice
- Crudités

Preparation:
1. Add water to a small pot and allow to boil. Boil the carrots 8-10 minutes, until soft. Drain and rinse.
2. Add all of the dip ingredients to a blender or food processor and pulse to combine.
3. Serve the dip with a variety of crudités for dipping.

Key Lime Mousse

Ingredients:
- 2 cans coconut milk, full-fat
- 4 tbsps. lime juice
- 1 tsp. ginger, ground
- ¼ c. toasted coconut, unsweetened
- 1 unsweetened date

Preparation:
1. Remove the coconut milk from the refrigerator. Flip cans over and open from the bottom. Pour off the liquid into a separate bowl.
2. Add the thick coconut "cream" from the cans to a blender or food processor.
3. Add the lime juice and ginger, and date (if using), and blend until thick and creamy.
4. Spoon into 4 individual serving bowls and chill for at least 1 hour.
5. Serve topped with the toasted coconut.

Loaded Nachos

Ingredients:
- 2 sweet potatoes, thinly sliced
- 1 lb. skinless chicken breast, shredded
- ¼ c. salsa
- ½ tsp. sea salt
- 3 sliced scallions
- ¼ tsp. black pepper, ground
- ¼ c. guacamole
- 1 tsp. extra-virgin olive oil
- 1 sliced jalapeños

Preparation:
1. Set oven to 375°F (191°C) and line a foil paper on a baking sheet.
2. Arrange the sweet potatoes on baking sheet and bake until crispy.
3. Remove from oven and allow to cool.
4. Serve and top with jalapeños, scallions, salsa, guacamole, and chicken, or any other toppings.

Snickerdoodle Cookie Dough Bites

Ingredients:
- 3 tbsps. organic coconut flour
- 1 tsp. organic cinnamon
- 3 tbsps. xylitol
- ½ c. organic almond butter
- 3 tbsps. organic coconut milk
- ½ tsp. organic vanilla extract
- 15 drops vanilla liquid stevia
- ¼ tsp. salt

Preparation:
1. Thoroughly mix all the ingredients together except cinnamon and sweetener.

2. Form balls and coat with the cinnamon and sweetener topping.
3. Refrigerate for at least 2 hours.

Fried Turkey Nuggets

Ingredients
- 1 c. avocado oil
- 1 lb. turkey, sliced

Dry Mixture:
- 1 c. cassava flour
- 1 lb. turkey, skinless and boneless
- 1 tsp. garlic, ground
- ¼ tsp. oregano, dried
- 1 tsp. onion, ground
- 1 tsp. basil, dried
- 1 tsp. thyme, dried
- 1 tsp. sea salt

Wet Mixture (stage 1 AIP re-intro)
- 1 tbsp. avocado oil
- 2 egg yolks

Wet Mixture (elimination phase AIP)
- ¼ c. avocado oil

Preparation:
1. In a shallow bowl, whisk dry mixture together. In a different bowl, whisk the wet mixture.
2. Line a parchment paper on a baking sheet and on it place a wire rack.
3. Insert turkey meat in oil and chicken mixture and then put it in the mixture of flour to coat. Place the coated piece in a plate and do the same for the meat remaining.
4. In skillet, heat avocado oil over medium heat for about 2 minutes.
5. Add in the nugget and cook each side for about 4 minutes, until it is brown. When ready, move to the baking sheet. Do the same for the remaining meat.

Loaded Tropical Plantain Nachos

Ingredients:
- 1 lb. beef, ground
- 1 tbsp. minced garlic
- 4 slices crumbled bacon, cooked
- 1 tsp. garlic powder
- ½ large sweet onion, chopped
- ½ tsp. turmeric
- ½ tsp. sea salt

For Plantains:
- 3 peeled and chopped green plantains
- ¼ tsp. garlic powder
- ¼ tsp. sea salt
- 2 tbsps. coconut oil

For Tropical Salsa:

- 1 tbsp. fresh lime juice
- ½ c. chopped cilantro
- ¼ c. chopped cucumber
- 3 chopped peeled kiwis
- 1 tsp. minced garlic
- ½ c. chopped green onions
- 1 c. freshly chopped pineapple
- ¼ tsp. sea salt

For Avocado Lime Crema:
- 1 large avocado, peeled
- 2 tsps. minced garlic
- ½ tsp. sea salt
- juice of 3 limes
- ¾ c. coconut milk, full-fat

Optional Toppings:
- lime juice
- fresh chopped cilantro

Preparation:
1. Fry bacon in a large skillet and place on plate lined with paper towel. Crumble the bacon and place aside. Preserve bacon grease for later use.
2. In a different skillet, on medium heat, sauté onion for 1-2 minutes. Add in beef and cook for 10 minutes, until brown. Season and remove from heat.
3. Meanwhile as the meat cooks, chop the ingredients of the tropical salsa and mix them in a bowl and refrigerate.
4. Blend the ingredients of Avocado Lime Crema until smooth and place aside.
5. Fry the plantains in bacon fat over medium heat for about 3 minutes on each side, until tender and brown. Add coconut oil if need be.
6. Use the beef mixture to cover the plantains and put a layer of tropical salsa and add avocado lime crema. Top with lime juice, cilantro, and bacon.

Cinnamon Mini Donuts

Ingredients:
- ¼ c. coconut butter, softened
- 1 c. Cassava Flour
- 1 tsp. apple cider vinegar
- ½ tsp. baking soda
- 1 tbsp. Ceylon cinnamon
- ¾ c. coconut milk
- ¼ c. pumpkin puree
- ¼ c. coconut sugar
- ¼ tsp. salt

For coating:
- 1-2 tsps. Ceylon cinnamon
- 2 tbsps. maple sugar

Preparation:
1. Set oven to 350°F (177°C) and grease the pan.

2. Combine apple cider vinegar and coconut milk and place aside.
3. Mix coconut butter and coconut sugar until well combined.
4. Add apple cider vinegar mixture and applesauce and mix thoroughly to combine.
5. Add all dry ingredients and combine to form batter.
6. Transfer batter to the donut pan using a piping bag.
7. Bake for about 15-18 minutes. Remove from oven and let sit for about 5 minutes. Meanwhile, combine coconut sugar and cinnamon mixture in a Ziploc bag.
8. Put the donuts in the bag and shake to coat them. Let them cool, then brush with coconut oil and immerse them in the coconut and cinnamon mixture.

Sautéed Zucchini and Carrots

Ingredients:
- 2 medium carrots, sliced
- 2 medium zucchinis, sliced
- 2 tbsps. clarified butter
- 1 tbsp. olive oil
- 1 tsp. dried thyme
- Ground black pepper
- Sea salt

Ingredients:
1. Set a skillet over medium heat and warm butter and oil.
2. Add carrots and zucchini. Drizzle pepper, salt, and thyme and toss.
3. Cook while stirring occasionally until they are tender and lightly brown.

Sautéed Apples

Ingredients:
- 1 peeled apple, cored and sliced

- ¼ tsp. mace
- ¼ tsp. cinnamon
- 2 tsps. coconut oil
- ¼ tsp. sea salt
- Coconut milk to taste

Preparation:
1. Set a small skillet over medium high heat and warm coconut oil.
2. Add the apple slices and arrange them.
3. Drizzle with sea salt, mace, and cinnamon and stir to coat with spices and oil.
4. Sauté while occasionally stirring for about 8-10 minutes.
5. Serve and sprinkle with coconut milk.

Balsamic Roasted Vegetables

Ingredients:
- 3 c. cauliflower florets
- 1 tbsp. Dijon mustard
- ½ lb. brussels sprouts, sliced
- 2 tbsps. maple syrup
- ¼ c. avocado oil
- ¼ tbsp. black pepper, ground
- ¼ c. balsamic vinegar
- 2 large carrots, sliced
- ¾ tsp. coarse sea salt
- 1 tsp. thyme, dried

Preparation:
1. Preheat oven to 425°F (218°C)
2. Line a parchment paper on the baking sheet and place on it the ready veggies.
3. Whisk thyme, pepper, salt, maple syrup, mustard, vinegar, and the oil together in a small bowl.
4. Pour the mixture on vegetables and coat them by tossing.
5. Roast in the oven while stirring after every 10 minutes for about 30 minutes, or until vegetables become golden brown.

Fried Onion Rings

Ingredients:
- 2 onions, peeled and sliced into rings
- 2 c. coconut oil
- ½ c. arrowroot starch
- 1 c. water
- ½ c. tiger nut flour
- 1 tsp. sea salt
- 2 tbsps. olive oil
- ½ c. cassava flour
- mayo
- coconut aminos

Preparation:
1. Mix olive oil, salt, milk, and the flours to form a batter. Immerse the onion rings into the batter to coat.
2. Over medium heat, heat oil in a deep fryer. When hot, add onion rings and deep fry them for 3 minutes, until brown. Use a slotted spoon to remove to a plate with paper towel.
3. Repeat with the remaining onion rings. Serve with mayo or coconut aminos.

Plantain Tortillas

Ingredients:
- 1 lb. large green plantains, peeled and cubed
- 1/3 c. water
- 1/3 c. avocado oil

Preparation:
1. Preheat oven to 400°F (204°C). Line two baking sheets with parchment paper and set the rack at the center of oven.

2. Put all ingredients in a blender and blend for 1-2 minutes, starting on low and increasing to high. Add water to create a thick puree.
3. Divide the batter and form into 12 tortillas and smooth them on the baking sheets.
4. Bake for about 9-12 minutes and turn the racks. Bake for another 10-15 minutes, until they start to brown.
5. Allow to cool for 5 minutes and serve.

Orange Ginger Wings

Ingredients:
For the chicken wings:
- 2 lb. thawed chicken wings
- ½ tbsp. powdered ginger
- ½ tbsp. garlic powder
- 2 tbsps. arrowroot starch (optional)
- ½ tsp. sea salt

For the Sauce:
- 1 tsp. grated ginger
- 1 tsp. arrowroot starch
- 1 tbsp. minced garlic
- 1 tsp. orange zest
- ½ c. coconut aminos
- 1 tsp. raw honey
- 1 tsp. garlic powder
- ¾ c. orange juice
- ¼ c. apricot preserves
- 1 tsp. powdered ginger
- ½ tsp. sea salt
- ¼ c. chopped scallions

Preparation:
1. Set oven to 400°F and grease a rack put it on a baking sheet
2. Dry the chicken using a paper towel.

3. Mix garlic, ginger, sea salt, and arrowroot starch and coat the wings with the mixture. Lay the chicken in the rack in one layer.
4. Bake in the oven for about 45 minutes, until chicken is well cooked
5. As chicken wings are cooking, whisk together sauce ingredients in a saucepan (apart from scallions and boil on medium heat. Lower heat and allow about 10 minutes to simmer. Add arrowroot starch and whisk. Allow 2 more minutes to thicken and remove from heat. Add scallions and stir
6. Toss the chicken in the sauce and use scallions to top.

Roasted Cabbage with Lemon

Ingredients:
*   1 green cabbage
*   2 tbsps. fresh lemon juice
*   2 tbsps. olive oil
*   ¼ tsp. sea salt
*   ¼ tsp. ground black pepper
*   lemon slices (optional)

Preparation:
1. Preheat oven to 450°F (232°C). Grease olive oil to a roasting pan.
2. Cut cabbage into wedges that are of size. Arrange wedges on roasting pan in one layer.
3. Whisk lemon juice and olive oil together and brush the wedges on both sides (top & bottom). Season with pepper and salt.
4. Roast the cabbage until brown and well cooked, or for 10-15 minutes.
5. Serve with a squeeze of lemon if desired.

Roasted Carrots and Mushrooms

Ingredients:
*   8 lbs. carrots
*   8 lbs. mushrooms, sliced

- ½ tsp. dried thyme
- 2 tbsps. olive oil
- ¼ tsp. black pepper, ground
- ¼ tsp. salt
- freshly chopped parsley for garnish (optional)

Preparation:
1. Preheat oven to 350°F (177°C)
2. If need be, peel carrots. Slice them diagonally ¼ in. thick. Toss them with pepper, salt, thyme, and olive oil.
3. Place the carrots on a roasting pan. Put in the oven and roast for about 15 minutes.
4. Toss the mushrooms using 1 tbsp. of olive oil
5. After 15 minutes, remove from oven and add in the mushroom. Roast for additional 12-15 minutes.
6. Serve and garnish with parsley if desired.

Roasted Sweet Potato Wedges

Ingredients:
- 4 sweet potatoes, wedged
- 1 tbsp. herb de Provence
- 2 tbsps. olive oil
- ¼ tsp. pepper

- ¼ tsp. salt

Preparation:
1. Preheat oven to 425°F (218°C). Line a parchment paper on a baking sheet.
2. Toss the wedges in herbs and olive oil and season with pepper and salt.
3. Put the wedges on baking sheet with the side without skin facing down and cook for about 21-25 minutes. Turn them over and cook for a few more minutes and serve.

Hawaiian Chicken Kebabs

Ingredients:
- 1 lb. skinless and boneless chicken breasts, chopped
- 2 tbsps. coconut oil, melted
- 1 sliced pineapple
- 1 organic red onion, sliced
- 2 chopped organic zucchinis
- sea salt
- 1 package small organic mushrooms

Marinade:
- 1 tbsp. raw honey
- ½ c. coconut aminos
- 1 c. fresh pineapple juice
- 2 minced cloves garlic

Preparation:
1. Heat garlic, honey, coconut aminos, and pineapple juice in a saucepan almost to a boil and stir to blend flavors. Set aside to cool.
2. Put the chicken in a container and add in the marinade to coat the chicken. Refrigerate for 30 minutes to marinate.
3. As chicken marinates, put mushrooms and zucchini in a bowl and toss with salt and coconut oil.
4. Preheat grill to medium heat.

5. Evenly skewer chicken and vegetables, alternating.
6. Cook kebabs on the preheated grill until brown, or for 9-10 minutes and then flip and cook the other side for 99-10 minutes.

AIP-approved flavors

a.   Spices, Herbs, and Sauces.

Which spices are allowed on the AIP diet? At first, it can seem like there's a really long list of ingredients that should be avoided. So just focus on the ones you can have. Here's a list of the spices that can be used freely, even during the strictest phase of the autoimmune protocol.

Lemon balm
Basil leaves
Bay leaves
Chamomile
Chervil
Coriander leaf/Cilantro
Chives
Cinnamon
Cloves
Curry leaves
Dill
Fennel bulb
Fennel leaf
Garlic
Garlic powder
Ginger
Horseradish root
Kaffir lime leaves
Lavender
Lemongrass
Mace
Marjoram
Onion powder
Oregano
Parsley
Peppermint
Rocket/Arugula
Rosemary
Saffron

Sage
Salt
Savory
Spearmint
Tarragon
Thyme
Truffle/Truffle salt
Turmeric
Vanilla (extract OK if cooked or use vanilla powder)
Wasabi
Watercress

Basil leaves

Peppery, fragrant, and fruity. Basil is traditionally paired with mozzarella and tomato in a classic Italian "tricolor" salad, and a few leaves ripped into a tomato sauce (or no-mato sauce) just before serving gives a vibrant freshness and sweetness. Basil is a delicate herb, and it's best sprinkled over hot dishes towards the end of cooking. As for storage, basil shouldn't be kept in the fridge, where the low temperatures turn the leaves black and limp. Keep it at room temperature and utilize it as soon as possible after purchase. A bunch of basil won't keep for long on the countertop or in the cupboard.

Balsamic vinegar

Balsamic vinegar gives a richness to a whole variety of dishes. It adds a roundness, a bit like a rich, deep-flavored red wine to salad dressings, roasted and grilled meats, and marinades.

Bay leaves

Often bought dried, bay leaves are added to stews for a rich, slightly earthy flavor, and they're good thrown in the pan when frying fish, too. Rather than eaten, they're usually removed and discarded once they've had a chance to infuse their flavor into the dish. Bay leaves are common in French cooking and form part of a typical *bouquet garni* - a bundle of herbs tied up and left to infuse a dish while it cooks.

Chives

Chives belong to the allium (onion) family. The long, deep-green tubular blades look a bit like grass, and it has a distinctive, mild, onion-like taste. Chives are beautiful sprinkled over fish, chicken, pork, and most vegetables. Snip the chives into small pieces and beat into sweet potato mash. Don't be tempted to leave the chives on heat too long and cook them - they're quite chewy and not easy to eat this way. For best results, snip them into small pieces with scissors or cut them with a sharp knife. Chives can be kept in the fridge until needed.

Coriander leaf/cilantro

This is a bright green leaf with frilly edges and is commonly used in Indian cuisine, to add color and contrast to a dish, as well as decorate a curry or stew. Coriander leaf gives a fragrant, almost citrussy, lime-like flavor. Big handfuls of the leaves can be eaten over an aromatic curry, or over a pulled pork salad. A bunch of coriander can be stored in the fridge, but use it as soon as possible. It doesn't have a very long shelf life once cut. It's worth noting that coriander leaves are AIP-compliant, but the seed (as in ground coriander) isn't.

Cinnamon

Cinnamon is a warm spice for flavoring fruit and sweeter dishes, but it's also one of the ingredients to use for Indian-style curries, because it adds warmth. Buy it in ground form and add a pinch or a spoonful to a recipe or buy it as a cinnamon stick and leave it to infuse, like when making a chai tea. Try a pinch of cinnamon over coconut manna or in whipped coconut cream to add warmth to a dessert. Cinnamon is traditionally paired with apples, but it's also fantastic with pears, berries, and oranges, too.

Cloves

Buy cloves whole or ground. Ground cloves is a dark powder and are needed in small amounts to add a warm, autumnal spice to a recipe. Too much and it could overpower the dish. Whole cloves are often dropped into a liquid or stew while it cooks - this gives a slightly more muted flavor than just using ground cloves. The warm, wintery tone of cloves complement oranges but also apples and most other fruits. The tiny cloves are also traditionally pressed into gammon or ham before roasting.

Dill

This leafy, aromatic herb has a beautiful aniseed flavor, which works perfectly with fish such as salmon and helps to cut some of the fattiness of the dish. Try adding chopped dill to tuna salads, sardines, or mackerel. It's also beautiful with white sweet potatoes and parsnips. When scattering dill over fish dishes, the bright green, feathery leaves give a beautiful contrast to the fish, whether it's a pale seabass or a coral salmon fillet. Dill is often used in pickle recipes and is also popular in Scandinavian cooking.

Fennel

Fennel has a similar flavor to dill, only slightly sweeter and more mild. Eat the feathery fronds as well as the striped, crunchy bulb. Either will give a sweet aniseed flavor.

Garlic

Garlic is common to many dishes; always have a bulb or two on hand in the fridge. The best thing about this pungent bulb is that it's so versatile. It can be used chopped, grated, sliced, roasted, smoked, fermented, fresh, or in powder form. It can be used raw or cooked.

Ginger

Ginger is such a staple ingredient in cooking. If one feels a bit under the weather, make a simple ginger tea by infusing a chunky slice in hot water for a few minutes and then sipping it. It really does seem to settle the stomach. It adds an incredible citrussy-spicy flavor to stir-fries and stews, too. Ground ginger is handy for marinades and curries, and although it doesn't have quite the same citrus-freshness and spice that fresh ginger has, it's definitely worth keeping on hand in the kitchen.

Horseradish

Horseradish is from the same family as wasabi and will help clear the sinuses in case of a cold! It's a long, knobby root that looks a bit like a thick twig or branch from a tree. Once it's peeled, the pearly-white flesh underneath can be seen. Grate it and add to dressings or stews, or make a traditional-style horseradish sauce that's great with steak or roast beef. As well as beef, horseradish pairs really well with smoked fish and beetroot. Keep it in the fridge after purchase.

Kaffir Lime Leaves

These leaves of a lime tree are most often bought dried. They do add a mild citrus-flavor to dishes. Add a couple to a beef curry or a Thai-style soup or stew, for added flavor. The leaves are removed before serving.

Lemongrass

These papery sticks don't look like much but peel off the outer layers of their covering and they smell incredible. They taste a bit like a cross between lime and lemon, and they have a sweet flavor. The lemongrass stalks have a coarse texture, though. One can either trim the stalks and cut them in half, dropping into a soup or stew to let them infuse their flavor, or chop them up and blend using a high-powered blender to make a curry paste. Lemongrass is good with fish and seafood, chicken, beef, and coconut.

Mace

A pinch of mace adds warmth, and a sprinkling in a burger recipe or pork hash gives it that distinctive sausage flavor. It's another of those spices that needs to be handled with caution. Too much could easily overpower a dish, so use a pinch or two at a time. A good pinch of mace can also balance out the liver flavor in a homemade liver pâté.

Parsley

There are two main types of parsley: flat-leaf and curly. The flavor is almost identical, but many feel that the flat-leaf variety looks better in recipes. Parsley is a main ingredient of chimichurri salsa and is perfect for everyday dressings and marinades. It pairs brilliantly with lemon and other herbs like thyme and coriander. Sprinkle a roughly chopped handful of the leaves over a stew to add color just before serving. Parsley is also a popular ingredient in smoothies.

Mint

Mint grows in abundance. Where it's planted it often takes over other neighboring plants. And that's kind of good, because mint is a really versatile herb. Finely chop it and serve with roasted or slow-cooked lamb, or sprinkle into a cool, refreshing raita. It also adds freshness to a mojito-style drink, where the leaves can be added whole to the drink and muddled in the glass until they release their aromatic, sweet scent. Dried mint is available but make use of fresh over dried because the flavor is so different. Some chefs have started to experiment with mint in fish recipes, claiming that using a very small amount can cut the fishiness of some dishes.

Rosemary

This herb was the symbol of remembrance in Medieval and Tudor England, and it would often be hung up on special occasions like weddings or made into wreaths and placed at graves. It's a very strong, sweet smelling herb. Rosemary is a robust, woody herb, and stands up well to the heat of an oven or grill. Traditionally it's eaten with lamb but is wonderful with roast pork, beef, and chicken, too. Snip off the stalks and wash them. Chop them finely before adding to recipes or strew the pine-like leaves over the meat before roasting. Rosemary works wonderfully with lemon and other citrus fruits and roasted starchy veggies and is also often added to hot and cold drinks.

Saffron

Saffron is the world's most expensive herb. These tiny strands are bright amber in color and come from a crocus flower. As well as brightly staining dishes a beautiful sunset orange color, they have an earthy, sweet flavor. It's one of the main herbs used in a Spanish Paella and can be used in sweet dishes or on citrus fruits, chicken, and fish. The strands are either added to the recipe as they are, or left to infuse a little boiling water before this is poured into the dish. Try a pinch of saffron in a dessert with oranges or lemons for something a bit more unusual.

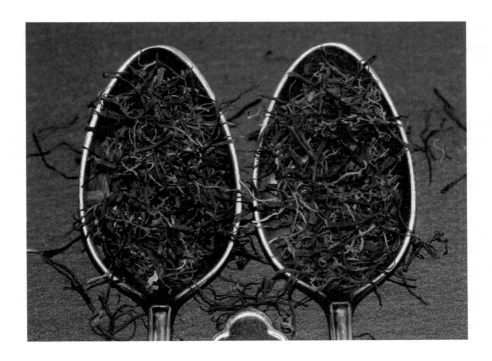

Sage

This ancient herb is thought to be good for the skin and is a natural antiseptic. The leaves can be quite large. They're a muted, forest-green color and slightly grainy and textured, with one side usually paler in color than the other. The leaves are incredible when picked off the stem and fried in oil for a minute or two on each side until they turn crisp and dark. The frying seems to concentrate their earthy, clean flavor. Save the scented oil and trickle it over the dish or dress a salad with it. Sage is traditionally served with chicken or pork, but it's also very good with turkey. Despite its appearance, sage isn't as delicate as some of the other herbs and can withstand some cooking. Depending on how long it is cooked, it will either soften in the pan (like it does when making a minced meat hash) or will turn crisp and crunchy when fried in oil or roasted. Try it with sweet potatoes and squash, too.

Salt

Salt isn't an herb or a spice, but a mineral. However, it's included here because of the flavor it lends to any dish. And while it is normal to add salt to savory dishes, sweet dishes can benefit from a pinch of salt, too. In fact, it can trick the human tastebuds into imagining a dessert is actually sweeter. For best results, and a better flavor that tastes just like the sea, go for sea salt. Flakes, crystals, ground salt, Pink Himalayan, or smoked salt can be used which adds a beautiful, slightly charred flavor to marinades and rubs.

Tarragon

Often used in French cooking, the leaves are delicate and have a strong, aromatic, aniseed flavor. It has been most often used as a partner to chicken but can also be eaten with oily fish, including sardines and mackerel. Tarragon is also great with lamb. The clean aniseed from the leaves cuts any fattiness from the lamb and lifts the flavor. Fresh tarragon can be hard to come by, so dried tarragon is used in its place.

Thyme
Like rosemary, thyme is another woody herb. It has thin, woody stems and tiny, fragile-looking, green leaves. Give the stems a wash and run your fingers down the stem in the opposite direction of the leaf growth, and the leaves will fall off onto the cutting board or roasting dish. Thyme has a very aromatic, fragrant, and sweet flavor. It's amazing on mushrooms and roasted meats and pairs well with rosemary and bay. Keep a pot of dried thyme on hand and sprinkle over vegetables before roasting. It's also a good herb to use to make spice rubs and powders.

Turmeric
Turmeric comes in two forms: fresh and ground. Fresh turmeric is a pale golden, knobby root that looks a bit like a spindly ginger root, but slightly more orange in color. Cut into it, though, and a dark orange color is revealed that will stain pretty much anything it touches. Fresh turmeric has a zesty, sweet flavor that's similar to ginger but much less strong and spicy. It is aromatic and earthy and can be chopped and added to stir-fries or grated and stirred into other dishes. It can also be frozen. Freeze in a freezer-proof container and take out a piece when needed, grating it while still frozen. When defrosted and left at room temperature, it can turn soft and soggy and become difficult to chop. Again, it stains, so be careful, but the dried powder is much easier to add a spoonful to a curry paste or smoothie.

Vanilla
There's no mistaking the heady tones of vanilla. In fact, a number of studies have established that it as an aphrodisiac. Vanilla seeds or pods aren't AIP compliant. Vanilla extract (buy the best quality) is AIP-compliant if it's gluten-free and heated in the recipe. It can contain some alcohol, but this is burned off during cooking. For strict AIP, don't use vanilla paste. This black paste contains the pod and the seeds. Or at least wait until the successful reintroduction.

Watercress
Watercress is more of a vegetable than an herb. But it has such a strong, peppery flavor that can be used in recipes instead of pepper. It's also incredibly nutrient dense. It's high in Vitamin C and Vitamin A, so it's a good ingredient to have in the fridge. Serve watercress with salmon or other types of fish or with beef. Alternatively, it can be blitzed up into a Green Goddess-style dressing.

b. Spice and Sauce Recipes

Basic AIP Green Thai Curry Paste

Ingredients
- 2 sticks sliced lemongrass
- 2 cloves chopped garlic
- handful fresh cilantro
- fresh basil leaves
- juice of ½ lime
- peeled slice of ginger
- 2 spring onions, trimmed
- ½ tsp. fish sauce

Preparation:
1. Place all ingredients in a food processor and blitz well until smooth.
2. Use straight away in the day's recipe or scrape into a suitable container and refrigerate for a maximum of 2 days.

Basic AIP Red Thai Curry Paste

Ingredients
- 2 sticks lemongrass
- 2 cloves garlic
- fresh coriander leaf
- fresh basil leaves
- juice of ½ lime
- 1 tsp. grated ginger
- ¼ tsp. fish sauce
- 1 small beetroot, cooked

Preparation:
1. In a food processor, add all igredients and blitz until it forms a coarse paste.
2. Either use straight away in a prepared recipe or scrape into a lidded container and store in the fridge for up to 2 days.

Basic AIP Indian Style Marinade

Ingredients:
- 1 grated garlic clove
- 2 tbsps. coconut yogurt
- 1 tsp. grated ginger
- 1 tsp. turmeric, ground
- lemon zest
- 1 juiced lemon
- salt
- ½ tsp. dried coriander leaf
- ground cloves

Preparation:
1. In a medium bowl, stir in all ingredients. Use to marinate seafood, fish, or meats.
2. Use immediately or store for 2-3 days covered in a suitable container, in the fridge.

AIP-Compliant Argentine Chimichurri Salsa

Ingredients:
- 8 chopped garlic cloves
- 12g chopped flat-leaf parsley
- 4 tbsps. olive oil
- 2 tbsps. apple cider vinegar
- sea salt

Preparation:

1. Trickle garlic and parsley in vinegar and olive oil.
2. Add salt for seasoning.
3. Adjust the quantities of vinegar or salt to attain the needed flavor and then spoon into a container or jar and store in the fridge until needed.
4. The chimichurri gets better the next day, so feel free to make it a day in advance, although it will keep for up to 2 days.

Horseradish Sauce

Ingredients:

- 3 tbsps. coconut cream
- 1 tsp. grated horseradish root
- 1 tsp. chopped parsley
- salt
- olive oil

Preparation:

1. Mix the ingredients together until smooth.
2. Use straight away or cover and keep in the fridge until ready to eat.

AIP Sweet and Sour Sauce

Ingredients:

- 2 tbsps. apple cider vinegar
- 2 tbsps. runny honey
- 1 garlic clove
- 1 peeled ginger
- 1 grated carrot
- 6 tbsps. chicken broth

- 1 spring onion

Preparation:
1. Put the apple cider vinegar and the honey in a small saucepan.
2. Finely grate in the ginger and garlic clove; then add the carrot.
3. Pour in broth and bring everything to a gentle simmer.
4. Once the carrot is cooked and is completely tender, blend the sauce until smooth (use a stick blender in a small jug).
5. Garnish with chopped spring onion and cool slightly before serving.

Italian Herb Pink Salt

Ingredients:
- 2 tbsps. Himalayan pink salt
- ¼ tsp. dried basil
- ½ tsp. dried rosemary
- ¼ tsp. dried oregano
- 1 bay leaf

Preparation:
1. Using a spice blender or grinder, add all ingredients and blend until a smooth texture is attained.
2. Store in an airtight container.

Nori Salt

Ingredients:
- 1 tbsp. sea salt flakes
- small strip nori

Preparation:
1. Put the sea salt flakes in a spice grinder or small processor and rip up the nori into small paper-like pieces.

2. Drop them in with the salt and blend until combined. Store in an airtight container.

Saffron and Rosemary Salt

Ingredients:
- 1 tbsp. sea salt crystals or flakes
- ½ tsp. rosemary
- saffron threads

Preparation:
1. In a spice grinder or processor, blend all the ingredients until a smooth consistency is obtained.
2. Store in an airtight container.

Porcini and Thyme Salt

Ingredients:
- 1 tsp. sea salt crystals or flakes
- ¼ tsp. dries thyme
- 3 dried porcini mushrooms

Preparation:
1. In a spice grinder or processor mix together the ingredients until they're at the desired consistency.
2. Store in an airtight container.

Peppery Green Goddess Dressing with Watercress

Ingredients:
- 2 tbsp. olive oil

- 1 pitted avocado
- fresh watercress
- 1 tbsp. apple cider vinegar
- Salt

Preparation:
1. Place all the above ingredients in a blender and blitz until smooth.
2. Store in the fridge and eat up within 3 days.

Instant Rosemary Oil

Ingredients:
- 3 tbsps. olive oil
- sprig of rosemary, fresh

Preparation:
1. Trickle the oil into a small container like a cup, mug, or ramekin.
2. Add the sprig of rosemary and mash it gently using the handle of a spoon, to bruise the leaves and release some of their flavor into the oil.
3. Use straight away.

Chip Shop Style Curry Sauce

Ingredients:
- 1 chopped onion
- 1 apple, peeled and cored
- 1 clove chopped garlic
- ground cloves
- ½ tsp. turmeric powder
- ¼ c. chicken stock
- ¼ tsp. salt

Preparation:
1. Place the onion in a saucepan.
2. Chop the apple and add to onion.
3. Add the cloves, turmeric, and garlic and pour in the chicken stock.
4. Bring to a simmer.
5. Stir well as the cooking goes on, until the apple and onion are both tender and the stock is hot.

6. Once everything's hot and cooked, turn off the heat and blend until smooth.
7. Add salt to season.

Indian-Style Mint Dip

Ingredients:
- ¾ c. coconut milk
- 28g fresh mint
- salt
- 1 peeled garlic clove

Preparation:
1. Pour the coconut milk into a blender jug. Pick the leaves off the bunch of fresh mint and add them to the jug, along with the pinch of salt and the peeled garlic clove.
2. Blend until smooth, into a speckled, green dip.
3. Serve straight away.

Basil Oil

Ingredients:
- 1 bunch basil, washed and dried
- ½ c. olive oil

Preparation:
1. Place basil leaves in the bottom of a blender jug.
2. Pour in the olive oil and put on the lid.
3. Blend until a smooth paste is formed, trickling in a little more oil for a looser texture.

Reintroducing foods

How should one reintroduce foods? The key is to start small. Have a bite, then have a large portion of it later the same day. Continue eating and observe if there is a response in the body. If there is no response after 4-5 days, chances are that there are no antibodies against that specific food. It can be considered safe and added to the regular diet.

If you have a reaction to a food, you need to permanently eliminate it from you diet, as it will nearly always trigger the immune system, much like a typical food allergy. Reactions can widely vary in nature, from symptoms like "brain fog" and lethargy to insomnia, depression, and disease flare-ups.

Notes:

- Reintroductions should only be made once autoimmune disease symptoms have significantly reduced while on the AIP diet.

- Once you're reintroducing foods, eat small amounts of an ingredient for 2-3 days.

- Look out for the following symptoms that imply food intolerance:

    - Worsening autoimmune disease symptoms
    - Fatigue
    - Headaches
    - Stomach problems
    - Muscle pain
    - Mood swings
    - Heightened food cravings

If one of these symptoms occurs, refrain from eating that food and stick to the AIP diet food list.

Most people follow the strict Elimination Phase of the AIP diet for *at least* 30 days. There really isn't a specific timeline to follow because everyone is different. Pay attention to the symptoms and only consider moving on to the Reintroduction Phase if a noticeable improvement can be seen. Some people need to stay in the strictest phase for three months, while in the most severe cases, some people are unable to reintroduce foods without a regression in health. After the minimum 30 days of AIP, gauge the symptoms. If they're gone, it's time to start slowly reintroducing foods.

Level 1

When one begins reintroducing foods into the diet, add only *one* food at a time. Start with Level 1, to avoid shocking the system. Eat just a small amount of the food twice a day for two days. Gradually increase the amount of that food in your diet for one week. For some people, small servings are okay but larger servings trigger symptoms. This gradually system allows you to judge if a food is something to be consumed in small amounts infrequently, or if it's something that can be a regular part of your diet. If no symptoms are experienced during the full week, the food is considered "safe."

If there is a reaction, one has to wait until the symptoms calm down before trying to reintroduce another food. If it results in a bad reaction, this can take as long as a few weeks. If there are no symptoms and adding that food went really well, wait another three days before moving on to the next food.

**Add foods individually and not entire food groups at once. For example, "legumes" are a Level 1 food, but when reintroducing the food, try just one type (like green peas) at a time. It can be a laborious process, but then one understands *exactly* what causes symptoms and what doesn't. Here's a list of some foods considered

Level 1

- Legumes

- Egg yolks

- High-quality seed and nut oils (like almond oil and sesame seed oil)

- Berry- and seed-based spices

- Grass-fed ghee

Level 2
Once you determine which Level 1 foods can be part of your diet, it's time to move on to Level 2. If you learn that seed and nut oils are acceptable, now try whole seeds and nuts. If a certain seed/nut oil disagreed with you, it's unlikely that the whole seed/nut will be consumable either. Seeds + nuts (except cashews and pistachios)

- Cocoa

- Grass-fed butter

- Alcohol (in very small amounts)

Level 3

In Level 3, try reintroducing cashews and pistachios. Try coffee with grass-fed cream but no sugar. Fermented dairy, like yogurt and sour cream will be a big change, so spend a good amount of time gauging the body's reaction to the different types and

amounts. Begin reintroducing paprika and eggplant and bell pepper, which are nightshades.

- Cashews

- Pistachios

- Coffee

- Grass-fed cream

- Fermented dairy (like yogurt)

- Paprika

- Eggplants

- Bell peppers

Level 4

At this final stage, you'll add the foods most likely to trigger symptoms. These include egg whites, white rice, and the rest of the nightshade family. Reintroduce legumes and grains, but only if they've been soaked and sprouted. This makes them easier to digest. Remember, if a food triggers a symptom, do not continue trying to reintroduce it to the diet, and wait until you're fully recovered before moving on to the next food.

- Egg whites

- Grass-fed whole milk and cheese

- White rice

- Soaked and sprouted legumes

- Soaked and sprouted grains
- Nightshade spices
- Chili peppers

- Potatoes
- Tomatoes

Keeping a symptom journal

During the Reintroduction Phase, journaling about your symptoms is a really good idea. It keeps you focused and organized, and you can refer back to it in the future if you're unsure about a food or a certain amount of a food. What does a food journal look like? Here's what to include and why:

What you've eaten and the amount

In a symptom journal, record any foods eaten. It's best to do it right away to avoid forgetting. Also include the time of day the food is eaten and the serving size. If it's something in a package, record the brand, as well.

Food cravings

Food cravings are often the body's way of communicating that a certain kind of nutrition is needed. Write down the food(s) craved that day, so as to track a pattern and see if the body needs a particular nutrient. For example, craving potato chips might mean the body has low sodium.

1. _Symptoms experienced_

Write down your feelings after ingesting a food and if such symptoms experienced include stomach pain, gas, bloating, heartburn, joint pain, and so on. Write down how the body felt in general that day, because certain autoimmune symptoms like changes to the hair, nails, and skin will appear over time. It's not as if eating a certain food will result to the face developing acne within an hour. However, if eating a new food for a few days to a week and changes are noted, it will be understood that the food is triggering and shouldn't be introduced into the diet.

Bowel movements

Bowel movements can tell a lot about one's health. Record these and how they rank on the Bristol Stool Chart.

Physical activity that day

Include physical activity for the day, since that can have an effect on the fatigue levels and joint pain. Record the exercises done, for how long, and the time of day.

Stress and energy level

The last item to include in the journal is stress and overall energy level. The most basic method is to record the stress on a scale of 1-10, with 1 being the least stressed. Stress has a huge impact on the digestion and health, so it's important to know your emotional status. If fatigue isn't experienced, be sure to take note of your overall energy level.

Keeping a symptom journal is important during the Reintroduction Phase. Record and monitor each of these categories to get the most out of the AIP diet.

AIP FAQ & Troubleshooting

What is an autoimmune disease?
An autoimmune disease is a disorder in which the immune system (which protects the body against diseases) turns against normal, healthy cells, tissues, and organs, perceiving them as foreign elements. An example is the Hashimoto.

What Is AIP?
The AIP is a lifestyle program and a type of diet aimed at reducing inflammation, reversing autoimmune diseases, supporting health, and improving digestion. AIP has four elements: foods to avoid, foods to eat, a process of re-introduction of eliminated foods, and healthy lifestyle choices.

What are the effects of autoimmune diseases?
The diseases affect a number of body parts including muscles, red blood cells, joints, connective tissue, endocrine glands, and skin.

What makes the immune system work against itself?
The causes are not known. Theories suggest a number of combinations like environmental and chemical irritants from the environment, drugs, leaky gut, genetic predisposition, bad eating habits, and viruses.

What symptoms do people with autoimmune diseases exhibit?

Symptoms differ depending on the type of the autoimmune disease. It can range from pain and fever to fatigue.

How is an autoimmune disease diagnosed?
With presence of an autoimmune disease, the body will produce a number of antibodies and some will invade the body tissues. Diagnosis involves testing for and pinpointing the antibodies being produced by the body. Blood tests for the number of red and white cells in the blood and for the C-reactive protein (CRP) that shows presence of inflammation can also be used.

Are there treatment options for autoimmune diseases?
There is no current cure. One can reduce the symptoms by adhering to autoimmune protocol. You can also consult a medical practitioner about suppressive medications, and reduce stress, exercise regularly, get sun exposure, sleep more, and do physical therapy.

Can a vegetarian do the AIP?
This is not advisable since the AIP eliminates many vegetarian sources of protein. If vegetarians follow AIP, then protein should be supplemented with protein powder.

Common Mistakes

Lack of full commitment
Society focuses a lot on the success of the Paleo diet and how it is mandatory to follow the 80/20 rule to decrease pressure and make the way of living bearable. This means you follow the rules at least 80% of the time, and break them when the need arises. When following Paleo for losing weight or to minimize some minor health complications, this can work, but with an autoimmune disease, it doesn't apply. The 100% rule has to be followed. It's challenging, but the stakes are high and the rewards worth the struggle. Be fully committed to the journey.

Poor nutrient balance

Therapeutic diets focus on eliminating foods from the diet that stimulate inflammation and exacerbate autoimmune disease. Avoiding these foods is vital to healing. The immune systems will stay super active if continually prompted by food intolerances.

Conversely, the flipside to this equation is the healing power of nourishing food. Rich and diverse nutrition is required for the body to repair itself on a cellular level. Specific foods meant to help this process include seafood, bone broth, organ meats, healthy fats, and fresh veggies.

Speeding up the process of reintroduction

The AIP is hard to follow because it is time consuming and strict. A large number of people rush to the elimination phase and then binge on all the restricted foods at once. This automatically renders the entire strategy defunct. AIP is a great healing tool only when done the right way. It lets your body give you information about beneficial foods and harmful ones. Such information is noted during the reintroduction process. When the process is accelerated, the valuable information cannot be obtained.

Assuming that food is the only thing that matters.

Diet is just one among several prominent factors in healing. For instance, sleep deprivation stimulates inflammatory genes in the body, disrupts the immune system, causes hormonal imbalance, and may cause autoimmune disease - this is still under investigation. At least 8 hours a night are needed. The sleep has to be constant to achieve the healing. Sleeping less and trying to make up for it later in the week is not recommended, as it continues the inflammation process.

Stress is yet another vital issue to keep in mind. In most cases, people assume that stressors in life are out of anyone's control. At times, it simply a matter of making the hard choices necessary to remove the stressors. Or maybe you have to accept what can't be changed, but change how it affects you.

Lack of support

It is always easier to keep on track on a healing diet with family support or even family members joining you on the journey. The same applies to friends. Doing this process alone is difficult, and extra support is important for success. Have a conversation with family and friends about the AIP and what you need from them to be successful. If this isn't an option for you, join Facebook groups and other online forums focused on the subject.

Poor physical and mental approach

Starting off a new lifestyle can be frightening, and autoimmune practice is particularly challenging. Though a large part of this journey is observing a new diet, your physical and mental approach to it is also crucial. More focus should be directed to meals, exercise, and mental clarity. All of these changes can be overwhelming at the start so commence this journey deliberately because healing and progress take time. Start with reasonable minutes each day and devote these to physical activities.

Allow yourself enough time to growth. With a positive approach, healing will occur. Light yoga or physical activity will lower stress levels and cheer-up moods.

Concentrating on removal and not addition

The start of a new menu is always a complicated process. Even if all it entails is avoiding specific meals for a week. The AIP lifestyle often means cutting out favorite meals, but focus on the new meals to replace them. Get excited about foods like quality meats, fish, and nutritious veggies. Keep in mind that it is not about what to avoid, but more importantly, what to be consumed. Healing is achievable only when the vital nutrients are utilized.

Attitude toward time

Only one month on an AIP diet and everything good to go. Doesn't it sound amazing? If only all the things in life worked out in such a way. Advancement takes time and patience. Healing the lining of the gut to solve digestive issues entirely can take years, not just a month. Chronic illnesses only heals progressively when given time. Set targets by highlighting your goals on a daily basis, then weekly and yearly. This enables you to note advancement in all areas.

Batch cooking
As it is the case with most diet changes, preparation is fundamental to success. Particularly when cook time in your schedule is limited, it is essential to plan ahead. Batch cooking and meal prepping at the beginning of the week makes the AIP achievable. Prepping snacks and meals is an excellent idea. Get yourself on a routine and stick to it.

Overlooking the gut
The gut is the main focus of the AIP. When the gut is interrupted, living becomes tough. There should be no overlooking on the gut's state. Avoiding meals that affect the gut flora like eggs, gluten, and dairy products will give the body room for healing. Start off the diet by adding foods that help to balance the gut. Such meals include bone broth, coconut milk, sauerkraut, and collagen. Glycine regulates synthesis of bile salts and is rich in antioxidants that regulate inflammation.

Avoiding specific flavors and variety in food
Among the assumptions in the AIP diet is that particular tastes and diversity in the meals will have to be avoided at all costs. This assumption is not correct. Just because people are eliminating foods does not imply that individuals should be consuming plain meals. Just spice up the meals with herbs and spices to give it a new look. It's incredible what different spices can do to meals. For the texture and flavor, use some of the spices listed above. Get the right tools for the kitchen to improve the extraction of flavors.

Traveling on the AIP is unachievable
The thought of traveling with tummy issues will probably come up at some point. Having autoimmune problems and observing the AIP lifestyle sounds a bit tough, but it is still possible to travel. Simply carry along some snacks and a journal and do more exercises. Look up for the restaurants and grocery stores in the area to buy the required meals.

Classifying it as a diet
AIP is categorized as a lifestyle and not a diet. It entails small changes contributing to healing process and the comfort of life.

Dining out and other lifestyle tips

When on strict diets, individuals tend to fear eating out, worried that there won't be any options on the menu for them. Invitations from friends are turned down or restaurants to avoided. This can be a source of depression and deprivation. Occasionally eating out while on AIP is possible without hurting the progress. Here are some strategies to follow:

1. **Plan ahead.** Planning ahead makes a huge difference. When possible, familiarize yourself with the restaurant menu online and plan for what to order. Going to a restaurant without planning ahead sometimes does not work.

2. **Talk to the server.** Some attendants in the restaurant will accommodate customers by providing modified foods to suit certain allergies or diets.

3. **Have a few go-to menu items.** At your favorite restaurants, it's great to have the go-to menu items that can be relied on.

4. **Choose simple menu items.** The simpler a menu item is, the less likely it is to contain hidden ingredients that one cannot eat. A protein and steamed veggies is much more likely to be "clean" than a soup or a big fancy dinner.

5. **When in doubt, order something else.** If the server can't directly tell whether a menu item contains foods that you can't have, order something else. Better to be safe than sorry.

General principles and tips to enjoy AIP food at any restaurant:

- Be prepared for success. Always carry an insulated bag with homemade food like coconut yogurt or mango-avocado salsa with plantain chips to eat while out.
- Understand the NO foods and never compromise.
- In a restaurant, check the menu and order ahead of time for meals to be prepared that adhere to AIP restrictions. Don't allow non-AIP ingredients to be used.

Notes on sleep

Sleep is not enough not unless it is a restful sleep. During sleep, the body produces huge quantities of hormones that facilitate the growth and healing of tissues. The hormones include testosterone, erythropoietin, and growth hormone. The body is still able to produce these hormones while awake and active but only in small quantities. To acquire them in optimal quantities to heal from autoimmune illnesses, a deep and restful sleep daily is needed.

Sleeping should last somewhat between 8-10 hours at night. This gives the mind a break and the body a chance to regenerate. Set an alarm on your phone to remind you when to start winding down and preparing for bed. Blue light can disrupt sleep cycles, so when that alarm goes off, that means it is also time to turn off the television, close the laptop, and put down the phone or tablet.

Try making light, positive changes to sleeping patterns, exercise routines and stress relief activities. These factors should go hand-in-hand with proper nutrition in order to have a healthy and well-balanced life.

Conclusion

Now that you've learned everything there is to learn about the way inflammation can destroy one's health, and how the autoimmune protocol and cleanse can reset the immune system and restore health, you have all tools needed to live a healthy, active, and fulfilling life.

But no diet can truly replace proper medical care. Some illnesses simply must be treated medically, by a licensed professional. Consult a doctor before beginning the diet. Remember, annual physical exams and blood work are important, regardless of one's age, gender, or ethnicity.

Sources

http://thepaleopi.com/2015/11/16/results-paleo-autoimmune-protocol
https://asquirrelinthekitchen.com/reintroducing-foods-on-the-paleo-autoimmune-protocol-aip
https://autoimmunewellness.com/8-unexpected-benefits-autoimmune-protocol
https://autoimmunewellness.com/paleo-autoimmune-protocol-print-out-guides
https://autoimmunewellness.com/whats-in-whats-out-on-aip-answers-to-tricky-foods
https://blog.paleohacks.com/aip-snacks
https://doctordoni.com/2015/10/the-truth-about-the-autoimmune-protocol
https://draxe.com/aip-diet
https://draxe.com/autoimmune-disease-symptoms
https://drhedberg.com/autoimmune-paleo-diet-work
https://drknews.com/autoimmune-gut-repair-diet
https://happybodyformula.com/12-mistakes-to-avoid-when-starting-the-paleo-autoimmune-protocol
https://healingautoimmune.com/definitive-guide-to-the-paleo-autoimmune-protocol-aip
https://paleoleap.com/autoimmune-disease
https://paleomagonline.com/10-things-to-know-about-the-paleo-diet-and-autoimmunity
https://reportshealthcare.com/autoimmune-protocol-diet-try
https://thepaleoway.com/autoimmune-protocol
https://ultimatepaleoguide.com/autoimmune-protocol
https://ultimatepaleoguide.com/ultimate-paleo-guide-eating-autoimmune-related-conditions
https://www.dietvsdisease.org/autoimmune-disease-aip-diet
https://www.medicalnewstoday.com/articles/320195.php
https://www.mindbodygreen.com/0-17830/a-30day-reset-to-reduce-inflammation-balance-your-hormones.html
https://www.ncbi.nlm.nih.gov/pmc/articles/PMC5647120
https://www.parsleyhealth.com/blog/autoimmune-paleo-diet-aip-heals-immune-system
https://www.phoenixhelix.com/2013/05/19/what-is-the-paleo-autoimmune-protocol
https://www.phoenixhelix.com/2013/09/15/my-experience-with-the-paleo-autoimmune-protocol
https://www.phoenixhelix.com/2015/04/04/aip-food-pyramid
https://www.phoenixhelix.com/2015/10/03/top-5-mistakes-people-make-reintroducing-foods
https://www.researchgate.net/publication/319367859_Efficacy_of_the_Autoimmune_Protocol_Diet_for_Inflammatory_Bowel_Disease
https://www.saragottfriedmd.com/is-the-autoimmune-protocol-necessary/#nitric
https://www.thepaleomom.com/do-i-have-to-do-the-full-aip
https://www.thepaleomom.com/modifying-Paleo-for-autoimmune
https://www.thepaleomom.com/reintroducing-foods-after-following-the-autoimmune-protocol
https://www.thepaleomom.com/start-here/the-autoimmune-protocol
https://www.webmd.com/rheumatoid-arthritis/paleo-autoimmune-protocol#2
https://www.webmd.com/rheumatoid-arthritis/qa/what-is-the-paleo-autoimmune-protocol

https://draxe.com/food-is-medicine/

https://www.boston.com/news/science/2013/03/06/salt-may-be-a-risk-factor-for-multiple-sclerosis-and-other-autoimmune-diseases-study-suggests

http://www.todaysdietitian.com/newarchives/110211p36.shtml
https://www.thepaleomom.com/start-here/the-autoimmune-protocol/?cn-reloaded=1
https://www.ncbi.nlm.nih.gov/pmc/articles/PMC5647120/
https://www.health24.com/Diet-and-nutrition/Nutrition-basics/how-much-red-meat-should-you-really-be-eating-per-week-20180514
https://www.parsleyhealth.com/blog/autoimmune-paleo-diet-aip-heals-immune-system/
https://autoimmunewellness.com/fruit-and-the-autoimmune-protocol/
https://www.ncbi.nlm.nih.gov/pmc/articles/PMC5506195

https://www.myvmc.com/treatments/nsaids-non-steroidal-anti-inflammatory-drugs

https://www.phoenixhelix.com/2016/01/24/can-i-do-the-paleo-autoimmune-protocol-as-a-vegetarian/,
https://www.vitalproteins.com/collections/all-products/products/dr-sarah-ballantynes-collagen-veggie-blend
https://www.harmony-hunter.com/autoimmune-disease-aip-faqs

CPSIA information can be obtained
at www.ICGtesting.com
Printed in the USA
LVHW050927110820
662879LV00015B/347

9 789492 916020